LOWLAND LANDSCAPE DESIGN

GUIDELINES

LONDON : HMSO

Application for reproduction should be made to HMSO

ISBN 0 11 710303 9
Printed in the UK for HMSO
Dd. 293235 6/92 C60

Enquiries relating to this publication should be addressed to:
The Technical Publications Officer,
Forestry Commission,
Forest Research Station,
Alice Holt Lodge,
Wrecclesham,
Farnham,
Surrey
GU10 4LH

LOWLAND LANDSCAPE DESIGN GUIDELINES

FOREWORD

The lowland landscapes of Britain are the result of a varied landform, cultivation patterns, settlements and communication networks, often showing a high degree of diversity over relatively short distances.

The creation of new woodlands and the cutting of existing ones can cause major changes in the landscape, quickly altering familiar and well-loved scenery. These changes can be harmonious, and mistakes avoided, if they are carried out with care and long-term effects are accurately foreseen.

Government policy encourages the planting of more woodlands on farmland, and many landscapes can easily accommodate well designed new woods. This booklet is broad in scope and intended to give landowners, land managers and their advisers an understanding of the existing landscape, and guidance on how proposals for planting and other forest work can be designed in sympathy with the best features of the landscape. Prepared by the Forestry Commission's Senior Landscape Architect, Simon Bell, and based on many years experience of woodland design, it complements other Forestry Commission publications on woodland planning, practice and environmental aspects of woods and forests.

Gordon Patterson
Landscape Consultant to
the Forestry Commission

LOWLAND LANDSCAPE DESIGN GUIDELINES

INTRODUCTION

The nature of the landscape is determined by the natural qualities of geology and climate, and by the changes made by man's use of the land. Human influence on the contrasting patterns of woodland and open ground has increased through the long history of agricultural change and development, forest clearance, and, more recently, reforestation. These changes have led to a demand for more natural surroundings as a contrast to an increasingly urban, crowded and stressful existence. Woods and forests must therefore be an attractive and harmonious feature of our countryside. They have to meet the needs of society by producing timber, providing a place for recreation, and constituting extensive and varied wildlife habitats. Woodland landscape design aims to satisfy these material needs and maintain our pleasure in looking at the landscape.

The Oxford English Dictionary defines landscape as 'a prospect of inland scenery such as can be taken in at a glance from one point of view'. Scenery is defined as 'the general appearance of a place and its natural features from a picturesque point of view'. Human observation is a vital ingredient of these definitions. The landscape is more than just an area of land with its individual arrangement of features. It is also our vision of that area, which, in turn, is influenced by our natural instincts for survival, our emotions and our education, culture and experience.

The landscape can be defined in terms of natural components, human activities, and aesthetic qualities. Of the natural components, landform and vegetation usually have the greatest influence, with rocks and water in a subsidiary role. The management of vegetation, whether fields, woods or hedgerows, is the most widespread human effect, with buildings and structures on a more local scale. Aesthetic factors are concerned with the reaction of the mind to what the eye sees. Shape and scale have most influence on our personal reactions, and on whether woodland seems in harmony with its surroundings. These factors can be used to analyse the landscape and to guide the designer.

It is often argued that the response to a landscape is a matter of personal taste, at least in a particular culture at any one time; but there is much evidence that a broad consensus exists. Were this not so, urban industrial landscapes would be as highly valued by people in general as the South Downs or the Pembrokeshire coast. Only then does personal preference come into play, as between the rolling windswept plateaux of Dartmoor and the small scale enclosed landscapes of the Kentish Weald, for example.

Our perception of what we see may be overlaid, to a greater or lesser degree, by influences from cultural, social or historical sources. Some of these may be widely shared, others may be deeply personal. The Dorset heaths, for example, evoke the novels of Thomas Hardy. The sites of famous battles or places of ancient spiritual or astronomical significance can arouse strong emotions. Landscapes that appear to be least changed from the period or work with which they are associated are likely to be the most valued and the most vulnerable.

Landscape is our visual inheritance. Trees and woodlands helped to create many of the vistas and enclosures of the landscaped parks of the 18th and 19th centuries. These landscapes represent a contribution to art for which Britain is famous. They should be conserved and sympathetically renewed wherever possible. The widespread interest in great country houses and their parklands shows how important such landscapes can be to the national culture.

1. An area of heathland in Dorset, scene of Egdon Heath in Hardy's "The Return of the Native".

2. A mature parkland landscape attached to a country house. The groups of trees are precisely positioned to achieve the special look associated with the great landscape gardeners such as Kent, Brown and Repton.

Landscape Change and Sensitivity

For all these reasons change is difficult to manage, but change there must be. The question is not 'whether' but 'what, when and where?' People often dislike change, and have a natural reaction to alteration in familiar surroundings. In the long run change will only be accepted if most people agree that it is for the better. How well a particular landscape can accept change depends on its relative sensitivity. Depending on the character of the landscape, this can be expressed as a combination of its intrinsic quality, its visibility and the number of people who see it, both as residents and visitors.

The quality of individual landscapes is assessed by observation, experience and judgement. It is impossible to rank the qualities of two landscapes of different character. Many of the best areas of the national landscape have been identified as National Parks, Heritage Coasts, and Areas of Outstanding Natural Beauty in England and Wales, and as National Scenic Areas and Regional Scenic Areas in Scotland. The designated areas constitute a high base level by which to judge individual landscapes, but quality must always be individually assessed. Wild appearance, presence of water and absence of eyesores are factors which raise the quality of the landscape.

The visibility of an area is affected by its steepness and position in the landscape, as well as the extent to which people can see it. Areas at high elevations can usually be seen from greater distances, while those on steeper ground have more visual impact. These aspects should be assessed from maps and by ground observations.

The number of people viewing an area can be estimated in terms of the general level of population, number of houses and workplaces, and the status and use of access roads. Opinions of local residents must be given proper weight because of their long and intimate association with the area. The perception of visitors can also be instructive because their appreciation is not dulled by familiarity. Walkers are often particularly knowledgeable and aware of their surroundings.

While it is important to consider the broad landscape as seen from particular vantage points, it is essential to remember that the land in view is owned, and owners have their legitimate wishes and intentions. Any theoretical landscape design must be tempered by the very real concerns of landowners and land managers. Rural landscapes are working landscapes where people have to earn a living. A good design is one that marries aesthetic principles with an understanding of ecological processes and economic realities.

3. The Wye Valley Area of Outstanding Natural Beauty. This is a well known, much visited area of high quality which is therefore very sensitive to ill-considered landscape change.

Design Philosophy

Having considered the landscape and the influences on it, what type of design is appropriate? In Britain rural landscapes can range from being apparently wild and natural, where human influence seems minimal; through a range of intensities of farming, from extensive pastoral to intensive arable; to the urban fringe, where man-made features dominate. A standard design solution does not apply. There are areas where the nature of the landscape is such that extra woodland is not desirable, regardless of the quality of design.

The wilder landscapes are particularly valued by townspeople as a contrast to and relief from the pressures of urban life. Woodland has to be designed to look as natural as possible, especially in wilder, more natural-looking landscapes. This is done by blending the woodland with the landscape, by reflecting its scale and by sufficient diversity. A design will fail if it tries to superimpose regular, geometric shapes on a landscape of curving ground and irregular patterns of vegetation. Although the layout of a well wooded landscape can be geometric in plan view, variations in size and spacing of trees and the influence of landform introduce a significant degree of irregularity.

4. A wild landscape in a National Park where landform and natural vegetation are the dominant patterns and where human influence appears to be minimal.

5. An extensive pastoral landscape of low hills in Wales where landform remains a dominant influence but where the enclosures, field vegetation and young shelterbelts show a greater degree of human influence than in Figure 4.

6. A scene of intensive arable farming in Dorset. In this example the field pattern has been removed to create large scale but intensively managed wheat fields.

7. An urban fringe landscape where there are many pressures on the land and where the appearance is dominated by man-made features.

Interaction of Landscape and Wildlife Conservation

If woodland is well designed, wildlife conservation also benefits. There may be conflicts occasionally, for example where the scale of landform requires felling areas to be large but wildlife would be better served by smaller fellings. In such cases the relative importance of landscape and conservation must be assessed and priority given to one or the other.

DESIGN PROCEDURES

The character of the existing landscape is the combination and pattern of those elements present that categorise and identify it as unique or particular to one location. There are several ways of assessing character, one of which is described in Appendix 1.

The process of design has three main stages: survey, analysis and appraisal, and synthesis.

— The survey stage involves the collection of all relevant data, usually in map form. Sketches and photographs of the site and the surrounding area are extremely helpful.

— Analysis and appraisal is the stage at which the survey data are evaluated and constraints, conflicts and opportunities are identified.

— The final stage of synthesis consists of producing an integrated design based on the analysis and which meets the desired objectives.

8. Those elements which make up the landscape are best recorded on a sketch or overlay on a panoramic photograph as shown here. Illustrations of how a woodland is expected to look can also be carried out on photocopies of panoramic photographs. Here felt-tip pens have been used to show different species and different ages of trees in a realistic way.

a. The original landscape seen from an elevated viewpoint.

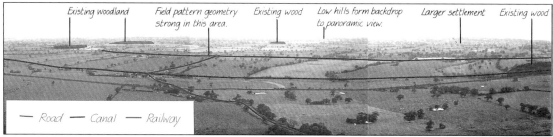

b. The apprasial of the landscape. The main features are noted on a photocopy of the view.

c. An option where small woods are tucked into the field pattern.

d. A second option of larger woodland areas.

Visual Design Principles

Much of the design process involves recognition and analysis of components of the landscape. To do this one needs an understanding of visual design principles, ensuring that the design can be adequately rooted in the existing landscape character, and aesthetic components are given due weight against functional considerations. They help appreciation of how elements of woodland can best fit into the existing landscape and how existing woodland can be managed effectively within the framework of a good design.

Shape

Shape has the most powerful and evocative effect on how we see our surroundings. Compatible shapes are vital for the overall unity of the landscape. Lines at right angles to the contour rarely look pleasing because the proportions of the landscape are broadly horizontal. Diagonal shapes look better. Appropriate scale or diversity will not rescue a design if shape is wrong; the mind fastens first on any incongruities of shape, especially those that are artificial and geometric. The distinction between natural and geometric shapes is particularly significant and plays a major part in forest and woodland design. The differing shapes of 'ancient' and 'planned' field patterns will also subtly influence woodland shapes.

    Analysis of a satisfying landscape often demonstrates the importance of interlocking shapes. One shape acquires a stronger visual impact from its connections with another. This can occur at a large scale, such as the pattern of open space and woodland; or at a very small scale, as between two species in a woodland. A high degree of interlock gives unity to a design.

9a. A woodland composed of several species of trees planted in geometric shapes. This looks very artifical, especially when seen on the side of a hill.

9b. In contrast to 9a this woodland includes much more irregular, natural looking shapes, the layout probably responding to vegetation or soil changes.

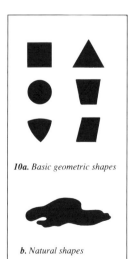

10a. Basic geometric shapes

b. Natural shapes

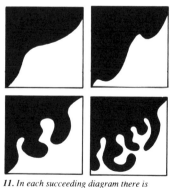

11. In each succeeding diagram there is increasing interlock of the black and white shapes.

12. The open space and the woodland areas interlock together, create closure and so produce a more resolved scale of individual elements as well as a more unified design.

Visual Force

Visual force is familiar from painting, graphic design and architecture. The eye and the mind respond to visual force in a predictable and dynamic way. The visual forces in landform draw the eye down convex slopes and up concave ones, the strength of the visual force depending on the scale and irregularity of the landform.

This is often seen in the patterns of natural vegetation. Plant communities from lower ground rise higher in sheltered hollows than on exposed ridges. Woodland shapes echoing these patterns match our expectations of what a natural landscape looks like. Shapes in the landscape should follow visual forces in landform, rising in hollows and falling on spurs and ridges, to produce a satisfying relationship between the two. Conversely, where the shape of a new woodland or a felling area opposes the visual forces in the landscape, it looks disruptive and out of place.

13. This black and white pattern induces a sensation of twisting movement.

14. This sinuous line seems to be wriggling or meandering in a serpentine fashion.

15a. An area of landscape in the lowland hills.

b. The visual force analysis. The stronger arrows identify more important features in the landform.

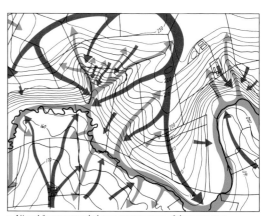

c. Visual forces recorded on a contour map of the same area.

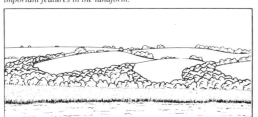

d. Planting in the valley flows up into the hollows following upward forces with the open ground retained on the ridges and convexities following downward forces.

e. Planting on the ridges and knolls is the reverse of c. but responds to landform in the same way.

Scale

The absolute and relative size of landscape elements have a major effect on perception. The scale of a forest or woodland should reflect the scale of the landscape. Much depends on the location of the viewpoint. The scale of a landscape increases the further you can see, the wider the unrestricted view, and the higher the elevation of the observer. The scale of the landscape is thus greater on higher slopes and hilltops than on lower slopes and in valleys. Areas appear to be of different size when seen from different points. Small shapes may appear to be out of scale when viewed from a distance in a large scale landscape. The generally small scale 'ancient' field patterns require smaller scale woodlands than the larger scale field patterns of 'planned' landscapes.

It follows that as the scale of the landscape changes, so should the scale of the forest and woodland shapes, with gradual change from one area to another. When a landscape or part of a landscape is seen as divided into two major elements, a ratio between them of one-third to two-thirds is usually the most satisfying. A hillside that appears to be one-third open land and two-thirds wooded, or vice versa usually looks more pleasing than one which is half and half. The mind cannot decide which is dominant, and remains unsatisfied.

16. In this view from a high point the landscape is large in scale. It is possible to see a great distance over the plain below.

17. In this woodland, views are enclosed so the landscape is smaller in scale than that in Figure 16.

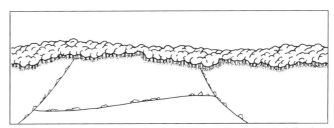

18a. Woodland occupying less than one-third of the composition looks too small and unbalanced.

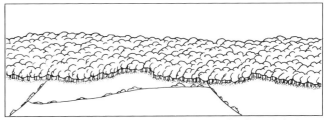

b. Fifty per cent woodland also looks unbalanced because neither element is dominant.

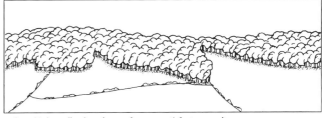

c. One-third woodland produces a far more satisfactory result.

Enclosure occurs when an element appears to enclose a space, and the element and the space become one. This can have the effect of increasing the apparent scale of small woodlands. Too much enclosure can have the effect of separating sections of the landscape and reduces the sense of unity. Enclosure is a useful device to enable small woods to reflect the scale of the landscape, and to give structure to a landscape which otherwise lacks it. Use of the word enclosure is not to be confused with the 'planned' landscape created by the Enclosure Acts.

When elements are positioned far apart they appear completely separate, but when close together they tend to be seen as a group. Nearness is another useful way to increase the apparent scale of small woods or clumps of trees, and to give structure and balance to a landscape.

The technique of coalescence can also help to resolve problems of scale. It is specially useful in flatter, more horizontal, landscapes where distances between elements are foreshortened. Small woods and trees, positioned so that they overlap each other when seen from certain viewpoints, give an impression of a more heavily wooded landscape that may be more appropriate in scale. Parts of Sussex and Surrey seem more wooded than they really are because of this effect.

19a. In this abstract example the six black bars are merely arranged in a row.

b. By turning the ends inwards three distinct enclosed spaces are created and the shapes become unified.

20. In this sketch the woods and hedges help to enclose space and by so doing they appear to be part of a complete composition.

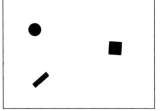

21a. Three shapes positioned separately.

b. When near to each other they are seen as a group.

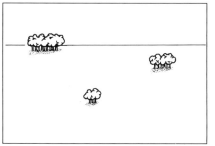

22a. Three small woods or clumps in an open landscape.

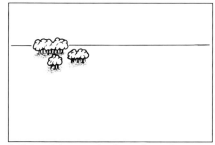

b. If planted closer together they tend to read as a group and assume a larger scale.

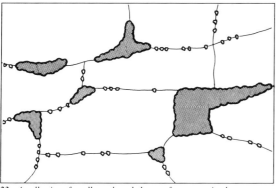

23a. A collection of small woods and clumps of trees seen in plan.

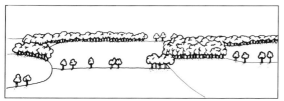

b. When seen in the view the woods appear to coalesce together and the landscape appears more wooded than it really is.

24. Belts and groups of trees coalesce to produce a well wooded effect in this parkland near Jedburgh, Borders.

Diversity

Diversity concerns the number and attributes of different elements in a landscape or design. It is a treasured feature of British landscape, the result of varied geology, climate and the long history of human settlement and land use. Landscape diversity is linked to ecological diversity, but the two are distinct and not necessarily equivalent.

Woods and forest introduce diversity into treeless landscapes, but newly planted woodland, whether broadleaved or conifer, can reduce diversity if it hides landscape detail. It is worthwhile creating diversity in an otherwise uniform landscape, but it should not be overdone. Excessive diversity frequently leads to restless confusion in a landscape design.

Increased diversity often has the effect of reducing scale, and may be used to do so where desirable. A high degree of diversity is more acceptable if one element is clearly dominant. For example, one species might occupy two-thirds of a wood with the remaining third consisting of a variety of species.

Diversity of texture, of different species and ages of trees and their density on the ground, can be very valuable. Colour diversity is also important, between species or at different seasons, especially autumn. Shapes are more obvious where the texture or colour changes. The different colours of farm crops and trees greatly enhance the richness of a pattern of fields and woods.

25. A typical scene in the English lowlands where the field pattern, crop and soil colours, trees and woods, and individual farmsteads produce a rich, diverse landscape.

26. In autumn the changes of colour in a broadleaved woodland landscape create rich seasonal diversity.

Unity

Landform has a major influence on landscape character, and woods and forests should be designed in relation to it. Woodland can be united with the landscape using shape, visual force and scale, and counterbalancing contrasts of colour, texture and form.

The scale of larger areas of woodland means that they have to be designed to blend rather than contrast with the landscape. Even-aged woodland is often highly unified and lacking in diversity, while contrasting strongly with open ground beyond, through darker colour, stronger shadows, coarser texture and vertical height of trees. These problems are overcome by designing shapes, external margins, open space within the woodland, and the pattern of species so that shapes interlock and unite the woodland within the surrounding landscape.

27. The interlocking of different species in this woodland helps create a unified design - where scale is resolved and the shapes are compatible.

28. This woodland lacks unity due to the incompatible shapes, lack of interlock and poor resolution of scale of the various component species.

'The Spirit of the Place'

When all these design principles are satisfied there will remain something unique to a particular place. This is a precious asset, and it is a challenge to the designer to work in harmony with that spirit. It is often expressed by particular contrasts or combinations of features. Enclosed valleys, or prominent hills; indications of great antiquity, such as old trees and rocks; earthworks; places where the lighting is dramatic, especially where associated with water; all these contribute to a powerful sense of place, particularly where there is a feeling of wildness. Woodland should be designed to emphasise these features, not hide them. Spirit of place is elusive and easier to conserve where it already exists than to create.

29. Here at Sherwood Forest, home to the legendary Robin Hood, these old gnarled trees are a special feature contributing to the spirit of the place in this historical area. They need to be kept visible and managed for their retention if the character of the area is to be preserved.

PLANNING NEW WOODLAND

The critical first step in planning new woodland is to understand the pattern and structure of the existing landscape. The design must be rooted in and unified with its surroundings. Sketches, photographs, notes and maps are used to record the strength of landform, enclosure patterns, views, and all the landscape attributes discussed above.

The next step is to assess the scale of planting consistent with the landscape type. It may be very difficult to incorporate small areas of woodland in open landscapes of broad sweeping vistas and strong landform. If new planting is appropriate at all, it should be on an adequate scale. Conversely, it may be easy to add small copses in a landscape already enclosed by hedgerows.

A balance must be sought between the woodland and open ground. This balance has to be maintained from all significant viewpoints, and may be the deciding factor in locating the new woodland. As a rule of thumb, a scene that appears to be more than two-thirds wooded can seem oppressive and important views may be lost. If the same scene appears less than one-third wooded, including hedgerow trees, the woodland may look out of scale.

If it is intended to plant under a Woodland Grant Scheme, it is worth discussing proposals with the local Forestry Commission Private Woodlands Forester at this early stage of initial ideas.

New Woods in Hedgerow Landscapes

The key question in landscape appraisal is whether landform or the pattern of existing fields, trees and woods is visually dominant. Small woods are a traditional and familiar element in the lowland agricultural landscapes of Britain, with widely recognised aesthetic qualities. If this landscape is to continue, it must be conserved and renewed. On flatter ground it is relatively easy to introduce additional woodlands where there is a small-scale framework of hedgerow trees. If a rectangular field pattern is translated as woodland on the steeper, higher and larger scale slopes of the uplands, the geometric shapes are seen to be discordant where they conflict with landform. The shapes are emphasised by differences in colour, texture and tree height compared with adjoining fields.

An early judgement must be made about the strength of the hedgerow pattern. Design is easier where it is still prominent and vigorous, incorporating existing woodlands within it.

The shapes of small woods need not follow landform closely where the hedgerow pattern dominates. The woods should reflect the scale and irregularity of the pattern, while interlocking strongly with open space. This is not easy; the visual texture of new woodlands, even broadleaves at wide spacing, is much finer than many hedgerow landscapes. On flat ground the even height of the canopy makes a horizontal line, different from the irregular crowns of spaced hedgerow trees. On lowland hillsides the new woods appear as shapes sufficiently distinct from hedgerows to seem geometrical. They need irregular shapes and edges to be in keeping with the coarser texture of surrounding hedgerows.

30a. A landscape where the enclosure pattern of trees and hedgerows is clearly dominant. Small, relatively regularly shaped woods should be easy to fit in this area.

b. A landscape where the field pattern has disintegrated and all but disappeared. Landform is not strong in this scene which gives few cues for locating small woods.

c. Landform is dominant in this open landscape. New woods should be positioned and shaped to respond to the landform as far as possible while allowing agricultural operations to continue.

The field pattern may be ancient, with irregular fields going back many centuries; or it may be more recent, dating from the enclosures of the 18th or 19th centuries, with a more geometric layout. Where both patterns are present, give priority to the older.

Where either field pattern is largely intact it is relatively simple to integrate suitably shaped and scaled additional woods which will reflect the existing patterns. However, if hedges are deteriorating, if fields have been enlarged, trees removed and the original pattern weakened, landform — even when subtle — begins to assert itself. Where hedgerows have been extensively removed, woodlands should be planted on a larger scale and shaped to echo landform, rather than attempting to reconstruct piecemeal the patterns of earlier times. The latter will appear out of scale unless comprehensively laid out over extensive areas. Larger, well-designed areas of woodland are also easier to manage, for whatever purposes, in conjunction with larger scale farming activities on adjoining land.

31a. Woodland belts positioned rather too far apart to create an impression of continuity in scale with the landscape of the Lambourn Downs, Berkshire (courtesy Pictor International).

b. With additional planting the scale of woodlands would reflect the landscape better.

32a. A landscape of ancient field patterns can usually be distinguished by irregular field boundaries, twisting lanes, irregularly shaped woodlands and clustered habitations.

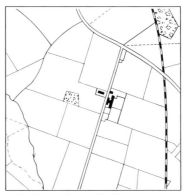

b. A landscape of planned field patterns can usually be distinguished by geometric field boundaries, straight roads, plantation woodlands and scattered individual farms.

New Woods in Open Landscapes

Where landform, in particular the qualities of different landform types, is the principal influence, it has implications for woodland design.

On *flatter ground* where the shape of woodlands cannot be seen, attention is directed to the way in which the trees are placed in relation to open space. Design usually hinges on the composition of mass and open space, the maintenance and creation of views, and the detailed design of the woodland edge. Straight lines can be perceived more readily than is often thought; use curved lines instead. The interlock of external and internal open spaces with the woodland is also important.

33. Some sketches illustrating how woodland might be fitted in to a fairly flat landscape.

a. The original landscape.

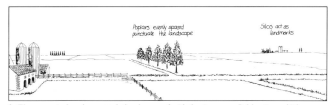

b. The appraisal - a large-scale landscape of wide horizons, no field pattern, little landform and lacking tree cover.

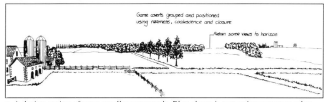

c. A design option of some small game woods. Plan shape is not as important as edge design.

On *gently undulating ground* the subtleties of landform assist design and flowing lines of woodland shapes can respond. It is usually better to keep open space in the hollows and new woodland planting on the rising ground, so that landform is emphasised. The scale of small woodland depends on enclosure and coalescence; a series of intervisible clumps on small undulations can appear very pleasing, provided their size and the interval between them varies.

34. Possible design options for woodland on undulating ground.

a. The existing landscape.

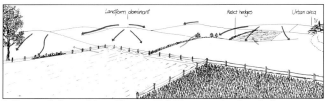

b. The appraisal - a mainly arable area with field pattern reduced to wire fences. Remnant hedges and trees are defunct. Landform is rolling and subtle.

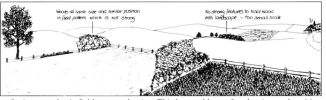

c. Option one : basic field corner planting. This has problems of scale, size, and position.

d. Option two : a game covert design where scale is resolved with some response to landform.

e. Option three : large-scale planting. This is too large in scale and creates too much enclosure.

f. Option four : larger scale planting which manages to maintain a degree of open character.

In *more rounded, humpy landform* it may be possible to locate woods either among the hollows or on the knolls. The choice depends on the scale of the hillocks. Copses on small knolls have a similar but more pronounced effect to that of woods on gently undulating ground, emphasising landform. If the landform is larger in scale an interlocking pattern of woods among the hollows may be possible. Relating shapes to landform becomes more important as elevation increases.

35. *Options for designing woodland on rounded landform.*

a. The existing landscape.

c. Option one : Filling fields with woodland creates geometric shapes at too large a scale.

b. Appraisal : A small-scale, well managed landscape. Healthy hedges but low numbers of hedgerow trees.

d. Option two : A more varied approach responding to changes in scale in different parts of the landscape.

Where the landform consists of *scarp and dip slopes* special considerations arise. The steepness gives prominence to the woodland on scarp slopes, and shapes should follow landform, rising in hollows and falling on convexities. Scale is important especially in relation to any unplanted ground above the woodland. The skyline may be critical and should either be entirely wooded or completely open. Views to the skyline from the dip slope may also be important, requiring the woodland either to extend down the slope or retreat from it. On the dip slope or on plateaux the rules for undulating ground apply, taking extra care near the skyline and where long views are obtained. Use coalescence and nearness to increase scale on the dip slope, if necessary.

36. *On a scarp slope these points are worth noting when considering how to design woodland.*

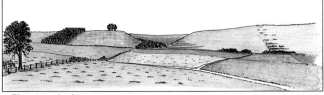

a. The existing landscape.

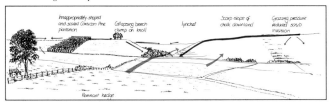

b. Appraisal : A predominantly open landscape where landform is important.

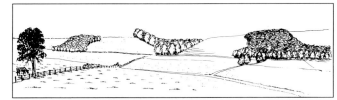

c. Option one : opportunistic planting when grazing is reduced. Loss of landform character results.

d. Option two : The sweeping, smooth character of the landform is retained. Planting is confined to field corners on the arable land.

There may be distinctive local forms due to unusual geology or geomorphology, giving a special landscape character and requiring careful evaluation. Examples include limestone gorges, some chalk landform and unusual rock outcrops or formations. Do not take them for granted. They are best kept visible and open unless woodland is a principal feature.

River valleys, flood plains and terraces are prominent features requiring attention. The upper part of a valley side may be seen as a skyline, while views into or across valleys may be significant. The shape of woodland on slopes of larger valleys should follow landform. Side margins, perhaps formed by ownership boundaries or subsidiary streams, may be visible; these require careful design to obtain diagonal lines. Terraces and other valley features often have pronounced horizontal emphasis. It takes skill to express the landform structure while avoiding a layered appearance. In these cases the design of the woodland margin in relation to the stream needs special attention. Smaller valleys may be better kept clear of woodland altogether.

Land reclamation may leave a landscape of man-made forms. These range from prominent hills created by coal tips to smaller scale undulating ridges on old gravel workings. In each case the general rules apply. The regularity of the landform may need to be hidden by the woodland; sometimes it may be worth emphasising, to make a contrast with adjacent landform.

37. This localised landform adds a special quality to the landscape and must be taken into account during design.

38. In this view of the River Wye the scale is large enough to accommodate woodland on the sides and some agriculture on the flatter areas along the valley bottom. The lower margin of the woodland is responsive to landform in its shape.

39. New Fancy Tip, an old coal spoil heap in the Forest of Dean, was reshaped and partly planted. The landform was purposely designed to appear quite sculptural since there was insufficient space in which to spread the material and reduce the gradients to match the natural contours.

Patterns of Small Woods

Woodland and open space form a strong interlock where a hedgerow pattern is incomplete. This contributes to the character and quality of many agricultural landscapes, giving a highly unified appearance from a distance. Successions of views from within the landscape, framed by trees, are seen as reassuring enclosures on a human scale. The more open appearance is easily unified with open ground at higher elevation, or where the tree pattern breaks down. These partial enclosures, with their outward-looking character, blend more strongly with their surroundings than the more enclosed fields of the Scottish Borders.

Those aspects of enclosure can guide the extension of an existing woodland pattern. Where the agricultural landscape is open, or adjoins an open hill, a generally 'branched' shape with outward-looking spaces blends well with the surroundings. Existing partial enclosures should not be closed off by planting new woods, creating inward-looking spaces separated from the wider landscape. Positioning woods in an outward-branching pattern often makes it possible to plant a substantial area in total while preserving the appearance of intimate scale.

An interlocking pattern is also more effective than an even scatter of clumps, which will appear too small in scale, especially near the skyline. Scattered woods often seem awkwardly separated and 'adrift' from the landscape. Additional planting should, if possible, link such areas into a pattern of broader scale.

Where trees in the hedgerows are more dominant, the location of new woods is less critical. Planted fields should not, however, be amalgamated into large geometric shapes incompatible with the scale of the broad pattern. Additional woodland can be sympathetically introduced if interlocking shapes are adopted. Any hedgerows completely enclosed within the new woodland should be partially felled, if necessary, to obtain the irregularity more in keeping with the interior of a wood. Any resulting coppice regrowth should be incorporated into the species pattern of the wood.

a. Complete containment creates an inward looking space.

b. A branching shape creates spaces which look outwards and interlock well with the mass of woodland.

c. An introspective enclosure may be unified with the landscape by partial opening or

d. by extending into the surroundings to create a more outward-looking landscape.

e. A careful balance of enclosure and openness can combine and blend a small-scale space with more open surroundings.

f. Additional planting can either increase the interlock or

g. reduce it

40. *The balance of enclosure versus interlock is an important consideration in woodland planting, here explored in abstract.*

41. Extending farm woodlands in a hedgerow landscape.

a. 'Branched' pattern of woodland well unified with the hedgerow landscape.

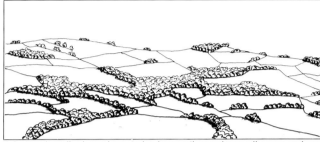

b. Additional planting which closes off spaces, separates the woodland pattern from its surroundings, and is too large in scale.

c. Planting which extends the interlock of open space and woodland maintains the intimate scale of the pattern and the unity of the landscape.

d. Scattered woodlands may be too isolated to contribute to the overall pattern, and may appear untidy.

42. Extending farm woodland in a hedgerow landscape.

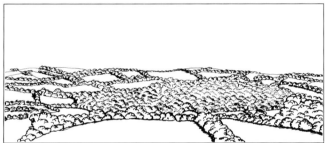

a. Although the choice of areas for further planting is less critical where the hedgerow pattern is stronger, large-scale geometric shapes should be avoided.

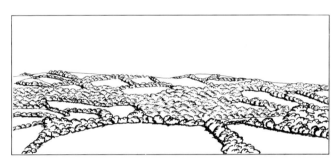

b. A more interlocking shape maintains the intimate scale of the landscape while allowing a larger area to be planted.

Shelterbelt Design

Small woods planted for shelter must be designed for this function, in terms of structure, width and orientation. There are ways to increase their landscape value. Shape and the contrast of woodland with open ground are every bit as important in shelterbelt design as they are for other types of woodland. The geometric shapes advocated for shelter in the past are not in sympathy with the landscape. The width of woodland belts should be irregularly varied, with enough breaks to interlock visually with open ground.

Small woods which readily fit into a lowland landscape with a strong pattern of hedgerows often appear too small in more open landscapes such as downland. Small shelter woods should only be planted where the small scale is appropriate. This may be close to existing woodland or hedgerows; on the lower slopes of valleys; or near (but not screening) features such as crags, watercourses or buildings.

As the number of separate woods increases, the small scale of their general pattern is emphasised, and often conflicts with the larger landscape. The greater interaction of different shapes further complicates design. An impression of extensive woodland can be achieved by planting shelterbelts so that they partially enclose larger spaces; or by locating them so that they seem part of an overall pattern.

43. Although this shelterbelt produces strong enclosure and achieves a good scale it is too geometric in a landscape where the field pattern is weak.

44. This pattern uses overlapping woods, clumps positioned near each other and coalescence to achieve good scale. The belt along the ridge provides an overall structure, although this has got somewhat thin.

45a. *Shelterbelts should not end abruptly on prominent skylines...*

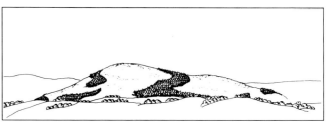

b. ... but should curve gently round them.

c. Shelterbelts should not frame the skyline ...

d ... without supporting woodland on the front slope, creating overlap and enclosures.

e. If shelterbelts are not planted on the skyline, they should be kept well clear.

f. Shelterbelts close to the skyline give intrusive slivers of open ground and the wrong scale.

The devices of closure, overlap and nearness can be used in various combinations to give an impression of larger scale. Overlap and nearness are generally more effective on gentler convex slopes and in foreshortened views. Closure is more appropriate on steep slopes and where there are important views from the space between woodlands.

Prominent skylines should not be outlined by isolated belts unless supporting woodland extends down the hill face in places, to improve scale. Woods should either encompass the skyline in a substantial way or be kept well clear of it. Belts ending abruptly on the skyline, or planted just below with a sliver of open ground above, look out of scale. Deteriorating shelterbelts on the skyline are particularly unsightly. If they cannot be maintained they are better felled completely and replanted to a good design.

Small woods look very artificial when placed symmetrically on hills. The impression of symmetry varies considerably from one view to another, so all public viewpoints should be carefully identified in advance.

Occasional clumps of woodland can be planted to emphasise points of interest in the landscape or landform. Prominent positions should be planted sparingly, otherwise the eye becomes confused by the number of points competing for attention. Where additional clumps are needed for game cover, they should be varied in size and spaced irregularly apart. They also appear less intrusive if viewed against the background of a larger wood.

These points apply wherever lowland landscapes are dominated by landform rather than hedgerows. The device of overlap can be used to good effect on gentler slopes to enable shelter woods to reflect the often unexpectedly large scale of the open lowland landscape.

46. Small isolated woodlands appear out of scale is such open landscapes. As the number of woods increases, the effect becomes worse.

Woodland and Farm Operations

The practical aspects of farm work have to be considered when planning adjoining woodland. Arable farming favours regularly shaped fields, so avoid choosing woodland sites which disrupt efficient machine working. Do not create acute angles at field corners that restrict machine access. Less manoeuvrable machines such as large ploughs may need reversing space at corners.

Arable crop management involves the use of herbicides and pesticides, normally applied as sprays. Small woodlands sited within an open arable area are therefore vulnerable to spray drift. In this type of farmland it may be possible to site woodland on topographic features that offer some degree of protection against drift. Headlands established for conservation and to encourage wild game act as a buffer zone between the field crop and the woodland.

Access routes through and between woods for farm machinery should be wide enough to let the ground dry out after wet weather and so avoid rutting. This is particularly important on east-west oriented tracks.

The siting of new woods on grazing land must be planned to avoid disrupting the efficient checking and gathering of livestock.

47. An arable field beside a wood. The shape of the edge is a sweeping, simple curve allowing machinery to work close to the boundary yet avoiding geometry.

Climatic Factors

Very dense woods sited close together can form wind tunnels. Woods should be designed to maintain a through-flow of air, allowing about 60% of wind to pass through at a reduced speed.

New woods should not be sited in frost hollows. Take care not to create frost hollows by placing woodland where it obstructs the free downflow of cold air on slopes. Avoid siting woodland immediately next to roads where drifting snow is likely to occur; this may make the snowdrifts worse.

Farms in the colder and more marginal parts of the country may rely on the drying effects of circulating air for maturing hay and grain crops prior to harvest. In these conditions woodland should be positioned so as not to be a substantial obstruction to the prevailing wind; the structure of the woods should let the wind filter through, rather than form a barrier that can create turbulence.

Established field drainage systems may be disrupted by new woodland. This can be avoided by constructing open drains round the wood that can be linked to the field drains.

Structural Diversity

It is often possible to incorporate some structural diversity into new woodland. In larger woods certain parts can be left unplanted, as permanent open space. These include rides, deer glades and water areas, all of which can be developed to favour wildlife and field sport. Some sections might be left aside to be planted later, to give more diverse ages of trees.

Shrub species can be planted in all sizes of wood to form an understorey. Broadleaved species which can later be coppiced are also worth considering. These features require careful design to get maximum benefits and to appear natural. This topic is dealt with later, in relation to the management of existing woods.

Choice of Species

The distribution of species within a new wood can reflect the broad pattern of the landscape; the pattern of ground vegetation; or the local landform, which will be hidden beneath the trees. Follow whichever is the more dominant in the landscape.

When planting bare land, the choice of species will be determined by possible limitations of soil and exposure and by the owner's objectives. A number of publications, such as *Silviculture of Broadleaved Woodland* (Evans, 1984), *Farm Woodland Practice* (Hibberd, 1988) and *Forestry Practice* (Hibberd, 1991), give guidance on this choice. Within the range of species chosen, the layout should fit the shapes of well-designed external margins and open space. For best visual effect one species or woodland type should appear to dominate the landscape composition by roughly two-thirds. Contrasting species give diversity, though too much variety is confusing.

The margins between species should be designed in the same way as other forest shapes. Mixing adjoining species at the boundary to make a 'soft' transition is desirable, but will not rescue a bad design. The transition should be created by planting a few groups and individuals of one species within the mass of the other, or by extending groups and single trees of each into the other.

48. A diverse range of species at good scale and in an irregular layout.

Mixtures

Intimate mixtures of species disappear into a general pattern or texture, and extensive areas of such mixtures rarely look right.
An overlapping and interlocking pattern of a few contrasting species, in scale with the landscape, gives better overall unity. Mixtures of conifers and broadleaves are the least beneficial means of increasing diversity. Contrasting trees are better introduced in shaped areas or groups, especially in sensitive landscapes. Planting such mixtures is, however, a useful way to establish broadleaves. It may be the only economic method of doing so, through early income when the conifers are felled. In landscape terms the chief difficulty is introducing enough irregularity to give a natural appearance without complicating management.

Row mixtures emphasise the artificial geometry of straight rows, heightened by the regular row width and spacing. Single row mixtures of broadleaves and conifers can be readily converted to pure broadleaves when the conifers are felled. When planted in wider bands the strip effects persist after the conifers are felled, often for a long time. Although mixtures in bands of three to six rows are silviculturally advantageous, they should be avoided on all prominent landscapes. These objections apply equally to row mixtures of contrasting broadleaves and to contrasting conifer species.

The visual effects of group mixtures of one species in a matrix of another are generally easier to resolve than those of rows. Peripheral groups positioned at the edge of the designed shape help to define the outline. The shape of individual groups is also important; squares look very artificial, while diamonds or hexagons with their diagonal emphasis are marginally better. Irregularly shaped groups are best. Groups distributed in lines running diagonally to the contour appear more natural than those in horizontal or vertical rows.

Varying the position and size of discrete groups gives variety, though over-large groups lose their silvicultural advantage. It is possible to distribute groups by setting out lines and spacing groups along them, but this runs the risk of producing a busy, confusing appearance. It is better to position groups irregularly within the outline shape by drawing on a perspective sketch, varying the interval between groups and avoiding straight line arrangements. Areas of larger and smaller groups are a useful device, using local variations in landform scale as a guide.

Further refinements are possible. Groups of mixtures can be located in a pure matrix, or pure groups in a mixture matrix. Mixtures of several species are probably best accommodated in groups of one mixture within a matrix of another. Such mixtures are complicated, not least in terms of future management, and are likely to be more successful in small, intensively-managed woodlands than in extensive forests.

49a. A woodland in Devon planted in a mixture of rows perpendicular to the contour. This creates intrusive effects.

b. Even when the interval and direction of rows is slightly varied and the line of species is broken in places, a row mixture looks unnatural.

c. When the small scale of the mixture is removed from the skyline, the appearance is somewhat less intrusive, but still rather unnatural.

d. When the row is curved, its appearance is less artificial, but there is still an unfortunate small scale on the skyline.

e. Curved rows kept clear of the skyline appear more natural.

Groups in the landscape.

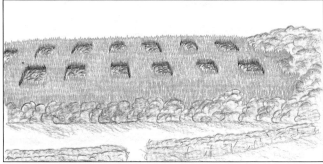

f. Square groups in vertical and horizontal rows look very artificial.

g. Diagonal groups in diagonal lines appear more natural.

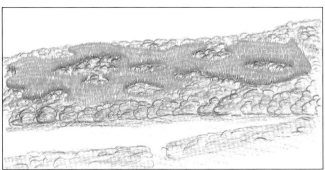

h. Aggregating groups eventually creates irregular shapes. These can be designed as described previously for pure areas of contrasting species.

A method of setting out irregularly positioned groups.

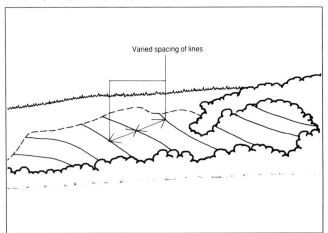

Varied spacing of lines

i. Shape the boundary of the area which is to contain the groups; then set out curving lines diagonal to the contours. The lines should be further apart at the upper edge or where they adjoin pure conifers. The direction of lines should vary progressively (roughly fan-wise) and should be a maximum distance apart of twice the length of the side of a group.

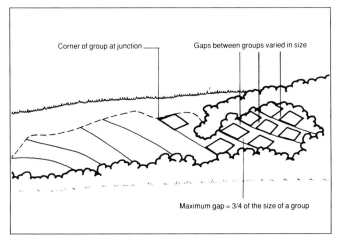

Corner of group at junction

Gaps between groups varied in size

Maximum gap = 3/4 of the size of a group

j. Starting at the outside of the shape, groups should be positioned each with one edge along a line set out as above. The distance between them should be varied, from one tree's space to a distance equal to three-quarters of the length of the side of a group. Mark out the complete pattern so that the outline of the groups is visible.

MANAGEMENT OF EXISTING WOODLAND

Assessment of how existing woodland fits into the landscape is a necessary first step when considering the visual implications of management. Many existing woods are relics of more extensive woodland, left behind during agricultural development because of difficult topography, drainage or soil. They are often unmanaged and semi-derelict, having suffered gradual attrition over the years. They may also be too small for effective management, as areas of wildlife value, or as landscape features. This last point is important where hedgerows have been removed, leaving the wood isolated among fields.

It is worth considering additional planting to increase the size and scale and to improve the shape of such woods. Study of old maps may help to show whether a woodland was once larger, and how it fitted into former land use patterns; this may give a guide as to how it might be enlarged. The *Guidelines for the management of broadleaved woodland* (Forestry Commission, 1985) give advice on how such woodlands should be treated. It is important to follow the guidelines if the woods are on the register of ancient woodlands held by English Nature, Scottish Natural Heritage, or the Countryside Council for Wales.

Work on existing woodlands involving new planting, felling and restocking, or other improvements should be preceded by an assessment of landscape character and sensitivity survey and analysis, so that all issues are fully considered. If the main viewpoints from which the woodland can be seen are identified, the visual impact of management measures can be foreseen and accurately designed.

50a. An area of low-grade broadleaves appears disconnected from the general hedgerow pattern. Powys.

b. Small areas of additional woodland would strengthen the overall woodland pattern, improving scale and reflecting landform on the upper slope.

Choice of Management System

Woodland can be managed under a variety of systems, all of which have an impact on the landscape. Systems of woodland management fall broadly into three categories: *High forest* is the term applied to those woods where the trees are of seedling origin; the tree in *coppice* woods arise from the shoots which sprout from the stumps of recently felled trees. *Coppice with standards* is a combination of the other two.

High forest is the predominant form of woodland. All natural woodlands are high forest. There are many variants, depending on whether the forest contains one or more species and how intimately they are mixed, the extent to which more than one age or size class occurs, and how the forest is regenerated. The simpler forms of high forest consist of more or less even aged stands that are felled and restocked, either by planting or natural seeding from nearby mother trees. The design of the felling 'coupes' (the individual areas felled) must be appropriate to the landscape and observe the principles of shape, visual force, scale and diversity.

Nearly all high forest woodland in Britain is managed under the system of clear felling and replanting. The system is easy to manage and regeneration is certain. It is the only practical system where the risk of windthrow is high.

51. An example of a simple relatively even aged high forest of oak. This has been well thinned so there is a good ground layer of vegetation. The stems are quite straight and there are few side branches.

Other high forest systems include the various forms of *shelterwood*. These employ a succession of regeneration fellings in which the young trees are established under the overhead or side shelter of the parent trees. Regeneration is normally by natural seeding. Planting can be done, particularly to fill gaps where natural regeneration has not materialised or when a change of species or additional species is required.

The uniform system removes parent trees in a series of seeding fellings, usually in relatively large coupes (10-20 ha). The texture of this system gradually changes as regeneration progresses, but the general appearance is one of uniformity. It is most acceptable visually where trees have well developed crowns and give a degree of coalescence.

The strip system is a modification of the uniform system. The area is divided into a number of narrow strips, usually based on the extraction routes. Progressive seeding fellings are carried out at intervals in successive strips, often with three being under treatment at any one time. When regeneration is complete in the first strip, a fresh strip is taken in hand, and so on. The strips are usually laid out so that felling proceeds against the direction of the prevailing wind. The geometric patterns of this system are difficult to accommodate in the landscape.

The group system involves seeding fellings at selected points in the stand, often where there is already some advanced natural regeneration. These groups are progressively enlarged, and new groups started. The wood has an irregular appearance both during and after the regeneration period; the resulting young trees often have an age range of 30 years or more.

Selection systems involve regeneration throughout uneven-aged woodland, taking advantage of seed years by small cuttings of one or a few trees. These systems are traditionally associated with forests in mountainous countries managed for protection against erosion and avalanche. The only substantial areas managed on the selection system in this country have been the beech forests of the Chilterns. There are a few examples of so-called single tree selection. The preponderance of light-demanding species in British woodlands makes group selection more practical. Here old trees are felled in groups of sufficient size to enable regeneration to establish itself. Selection systems are rarely practised in this country because of the intensive management involved.

Coppice woods are always the result of human management. In former times this type of woodland was widespread because the system produced the fuel and timber that people then required. Areas of coppice were managed on a rotational basis, felling so much annually or every few years when the coppice stems had reached the required size. Age of the stems at a felling was generally 20 to 40 years, depending on the species and site productivity. The individual coppice stands may be thinned, so that the final cut consists of stems of the desired quality and larger diameter.

It is possible to manage coppice woods on a selection basis, with a range of ages of regrowth on the same area. This gives greater continuity of woodland cover and more intimate structural diversity than conventional coppice. The system requires intensive management, but may have advantages for landscape and wildlife conservation.

With the relatively short cycle of felling in adjacent areas and a range of different ages and heights, coppice woodland can have a very diverse spatial structure. The ground surface vegetation is exposed to full light more frequently than under high forest, and this may benefit wildlife. Being deciduous, coppice woods can be dull and gloomy in winter, but in spring the field layer of flowering plants can be very rich. Again, shape and scale of coupes becomes important if the woodland is visible externally.

52. Strip felling in progress. This example, although in a conifer woodland in Austria, has produced the typical rather formal result which can fragment the forest and break the line of the skyline (see Figure 64).

53. An example of an irregular group shelterwood where the young trees are gradually given more light as they grow. A visually diverse structure of varying heights is seen from within and minimal areas are felled at any one time.

54. In the Chiltern Hills the beechwoods are traditionally worked on a group selection system. This view shows a well established group of young trees in an opening in the canopy of mature beech. The small-scale structure is ideally suited to producing the level of visual diversity appropriate inside the woodland.

Coppice worked on short rotations for fuelwood is likely to have a poorer internal landscape and wildlife conservation value. Such coppice woods are mainly seen from outside, where shape, scale and structural diversity become important.

Coppice with standards was once widespread. The system combines simple even-aged coppice, grown as the underwood, and standards of uneven age treated under the high forest selection system as the overwood. Standards are trees originating from seedlings, or well-shaped coppice stems retained when the coppice is cut, grown on rotations equal to several coppice rotations. This provides larger dimensions of timber than can be obtained from the coppice. The retention of standards over several coppice rotations makes for a greater degree of visual continuity than we have in simple coppice.

Many older broadleaved woods have the appearance of high forest but are actually of coppice origin. When the demand for coppice material ceased, around the 1920s, the stems were left to grow on to full size trees that had some sale value. The timber yield from these 'stored coppice' woods is similar to comparable high forest stands, though timber quality may be inferior. It may be possible to revive coppicing in these stands, even after 100 years.

Wood pasture and wooded parkland are combinations of high forest and pastoral agriculture that also had a place in earlier times. They provided both grazing and timber for local needs within an open structure, in which open-grown trees developed large crowns and great character.

Woodland is more diverse visually where the structure is more complex. There is a greater wealth of detail to see, and such woods tend to appear wilder and more natural. This is particularly so where there is diversity of tree species and several canopy layers. Woods have a high degree of interest when managed to give a good alternation of young and middle-aged stands alongside mature trees, and where adjoining space extends beneath the canopy. Light comes through the branches and understorey layers in varying intensities, fellings are unobtrusive and there is a greater sense of continuity and permanence.

The understorey is particularly important where a high visual carrying capacity is required. Dense shrubs or young trees growing above head height prevent people seeing each other across the woodland. This increases the number of people a wood can contain without it feeling crowded. Understoreys of hazel, beech or hornbeam are effective, while holly provides year-round evergreen screening and spatial composition.

The visual effects of shape and scale have to be resolved both in the layout of woodland types and in relation to the felling and regeneration regime, especially if the woodland is on a hillside or can be seen from a vantage point outside. Small felling coupes sometimes appear moth-eaten. Clear felled coupes of bigger scale may be preferable. Such coupes on skylines can open up views out of the woodland that may be valuable.

The design of felling coupes has silvicultural aspects that have to be taken into account (Evans, 1984). The successful regeneration of many tree species requires large enough areas to be felled. Most broadleaves are regenerated by fellings of one to three hectares or more. It may be necessary to reach a balance between silvicultural and wildlife considerations and the desired visual effects.

Where maintaining continuous woodland cover is a high priority it can be obtained by small-scale regeneration fellings, or by underplanting older stands to create understoreys, retained for visual cover when the old trees are eventually cut. Remember that these approaches require a high intensity of management, often over a long period. It is best to limit them to those areas where they are specially desirable. It is impractical and unwise to propose detailed and intricate management over extensive areas. The landscape design requirements can nearly always be met by simpler methods.

55. Simple coppice. The light reaches the woodland floor in spring allowing the field layer to flourish.

56. Coppice-with-standards. In this Gloucestershire example the crowns of the large branchy standards coalesce in the view to give a canopy structure, while the coppice regrows beneath.

57. The beech woodland seen here has a diverse structure over a relatively small area. Open space, young trees, middle sized and mature trees all occur near each other. This gives greater visual interest and allows the space to flow between and beneath the different stands.

Design of Felling Coupes

Coupe design is particularly important with clear felling, but is also relevant in other systems. Any change in the canopy has some visual impact. Adjacent coupes show differences in texture, colour and tree height. Heavy thinning causes change in texture, which contrasts with lightly thinned or unthinned stands and introduces shapes. Contrasts of tree size and open space also occur with naturally regenerated woods. Coupes should be of appropriate scale and shape, and are a valuable opportunity to diversify the forest landscape. Forward planning is essential to plan a complete coupe system that takes account of the timing of felling phases and the sequence of felling.

In flat and gently rolling topography the woodlands are seen 'edge on' and mainly from roadsides. The height of the trees and spaces within the woodland are dominant factors. Natural features are often scarce. The design of coupes, forest edges and particular stands should be made as interesting as possible, at an appropriate scale.

— Felling coupes should be based on curvilinear shapes, tapering away from well used viewpoints, roads or paths.

— Rectangular coupes are not acceptable. Old grid-system ride layouts should not be perpetuated.

— A semi-permanent framework of retained drifts of trees, open spaces and managed edges should be developed along footpaths and around recreation areas. Views and vistas should be created, especially along roads used by the public.

— Emphasise any minor undulations in the ground by starting felling on lower ground and delaying it on higher, particularly if the view is over slightly concave ground.

— More undulating topography can be further emphasised by shaping the edges of coupes on lower ground to rise in hollows between convex landform.

58. A felling coupe which has been designed with curving, interlocking edges, retained stands and an appropriate scale in this landscape. Bourne Woods, Lincs.

59. The designs of felling areas in flat landscapes.

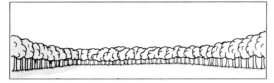

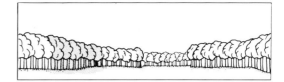

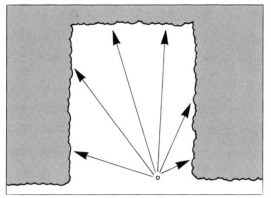

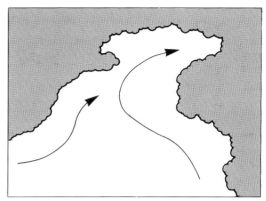

a. Rectangular space - the eye roams aimlessly seeking interest which is not present.

b. Shaped space - the eye is drawn through the space winding from side to side.

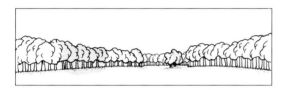

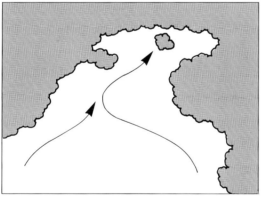

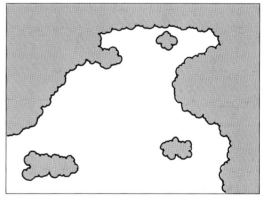

c. Shaped edges drawing the eye through the space to a feature.

d. Foreground retentions give a sense of depth.

On hillsides the coupe design should follow landform, with coupe edges rising in hollows and falling on ridges. Scale should increase from small at the foot of the hill to large near the skyline. Where forest clothes the skyline special care is needed to avoid breaking it in an intrusive fashion, such as across convex landform; or running into problems of scale by felling too small coupes.

When woodland occupies a prominent knoll or dome-like landform, the treatment of the cap becomes particularly important. Very small woods are probably best completely felled and replanted. Larger ones require small early coupes around the base to establish a scale and pattern before felling the cap, either as a whole or in sections, depending on its scale.

The hill top clumps often seen on downland may be well loved landmarks, and pose particular problems. Although too small in scale in relation to their landscape context, their continuation is often considered necessary. They are usually too small to regenerate naturally. Planting a replacement clump next to an existing one will often mean that it is not on the highest point of the hill or ridge. It will not look comfortable when the original clump is felled. The best course of action will often be to clear fell and replant, and simply do without the landmark for a few years.

These principles apply equally to broadleaved and conifer woodlands, but the timing of adjacent fellings requires different treatment. In conifers it is usual to allow 7-15 years to elapse before felling an adjoining coupe; broadleaves may require intervals of 15 to 20 years or more, because of slower growth rates and longer rotations, to get the desired diversity of woodland structure.

60a. Although the coupe is in scale with this small landscape, the retention at the skyline looks too thin and will seem even worse when subsequently felled. The shape is also too square.

b. Additional retention on the convex upper slopes; a possible alternative would be additional felling at the sides to improve the shape.

61. A medium sized wood on a ridge in Devon.

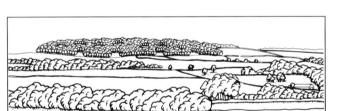

a. Very small group fellings below the skyline. At this stage the skyline is intact but shadows may show the coupes as small holes.

b. If the groups interrupt the skyline they produce small-scale regularly spaced breaks disrupting the otherwise smooth integrity of the cap.

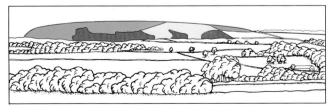

c. An alternative is to treat the wood by felling a smaller number of large coupes in scale with the landscape, controlling the point at which the skyline is broken.

d. At phase one the early coupes are located along the lower edge of the wood and are irregularly shaped.

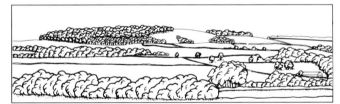

e. At phase two approximately one-third of the skyline is removed. The scale is more appropriate to that of the wood while the diagonal boundaries and the established regrowth from phase one help to unify the design.

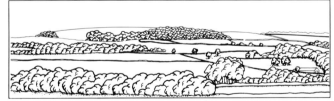

f. The third phase sees the removal of the remaining section of skyline, around two-thirds, with the regrowth controlling scale and providing interlock.

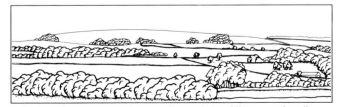

g. Another option, more appropriate to smaller woods, is to fell it more-or-less all at once, retaining only small foreground elements. In this way the complete wood can be regenerated.

The design of regeneration felling coupes under shelterwood systems follows the same lines as for clear felling. The main concern is the spatial distribution of stands in different stages of regeneration, though the coupe boundaries are often more subtle than in clear felling. Coupe edges need special attention, both at coupe boundaries and along access routes.

Edges, and occasionally silhouettes of spaced trees, are critical features where the uniform system is practised in flat landscapes. In more rolling landscapes or ones with longer views into the forest the widely spaced mother trees may create an intrusive effect when close to the skyline. Where scale is a problem in these cases it is probably better to design a shaped skyline coupe to be clear felled, with the shelterwood fellings confined to lower slopes.

A similar visual problem can arise in small broadleaved woods where it is desired to maintain some shade to woodland flora during the regeneration process. This is possible if large crowned trees are retained to give a strong degree of coalescence in the view.

62. This series of sketches shows that while a uniform shelterwood system only gradually removes the trees so that woodland cover is retained, the actual shape of the coupe so treated must follow the same principles of shape and scale as a clear felled area.

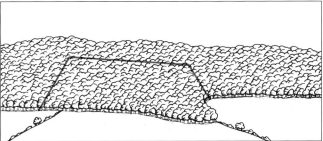

a. The wood before regeneration. The red line shows the area to be treated.

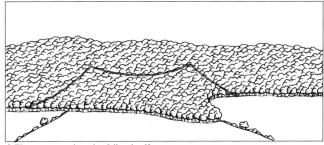

d. The same area shaped to follow landform.

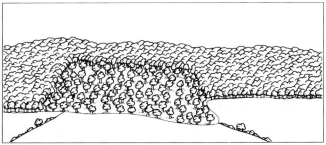

b. At the preparatory seeding felling the texture of the wood coarsens as the interval between trees increases.

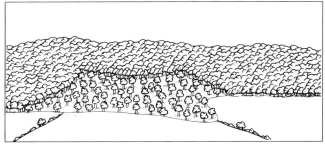

e. As felling proceeds the shape starts to show as coarser texture and the edge blends into the surrounding areas.

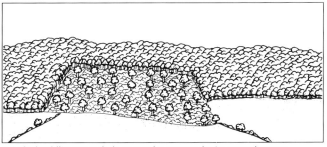

c. As further felling proceeds the area under treatment begins to stand out as a geometric shape.

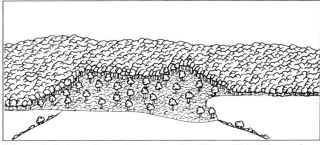

f. Eventually the designed coupe shape becomes clear. This would ideally be one of a pattern of such coupes.

63a. *A strip system laid out on purely functional lines can produce strong regularity, formality and break the skyline to create a very serrated profile. The formality increases as the fellings proceed although there is some blurring of the age distinction as the regimented strips grow.*

b. *The area to be regenerated under the strip system is kept below the skyline to reduce the impact. The skyline is treated as a coupe in shape and scale with the landscape and regenerated by another method. The strips are slightly curved to respond to landform, assuming they are accessible by wheeled or tracked vehicles. A retained area at the bottom helps control scale further.*

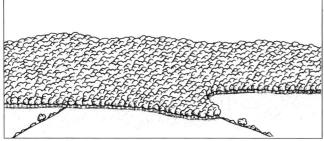

The existing woodland.

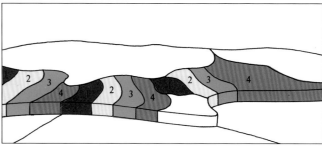

The coupe and strip design.

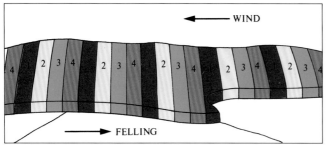

Strips laid out in traditional manner.

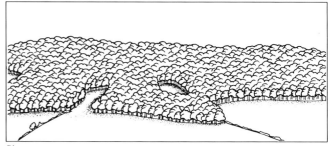

Phase one.

Phase one.

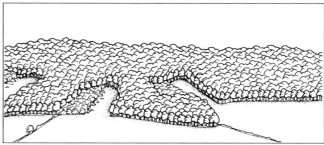

Phase two.

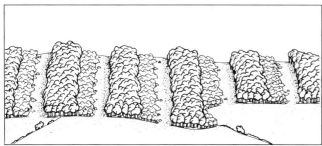

Phase two.

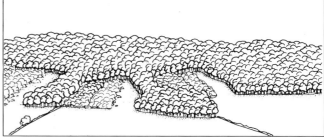

Phase three.

Phase three.

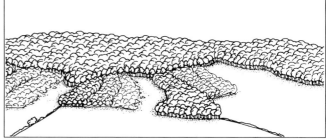

Phase four.

Systems involving regular geometric patterns of any sort present landscape problems. When designed primarily with natural regeneration in mind there are some silvicultural constraints on the shape and layout of seeding fellings. Strips can be given curved edges and variable widths, with some retained groups of old trees to break up the views and provide closure. This helps to avoid major problems in flatter landscapes.

Group regeneration systems involve gradual removal of older trees around naturally occurring or specially created gaps in a wood. A very regular pattern of openings gives a spotty effect on hillsides that can be overcome to some extent by varying the scale of fellings, making them larger near the top of the hill.

In flat landscapes group fellings can show up as a castellated woodland edge silhouette. This can be avoided by allowing some gaps to coalesce and overlap with each other.

On dome-like landforms the effect of equally spaced groups breaking what is otherwise an even textured skyline can cause fussy effects. This can be resolved by identifying the horizon line of the skyline from a selected viewpoint and managing this separately while groups are formed on the lower slopes.

The design of coupes for coppice should follow the same lines as clear felled high forest. Coppice with standards also requires a well designed coupe pattern for the coppice element. Choose standards with care to obtain crown coalescence, especially on skylines to avoid a straggly appearance, while allowing sufficient light to the coppice to maintain satisfactory growth.

64a. The even distribution of groups can produce a fragmented, moth-eaten appearance if they are all the same size and interval. The problem of the skyline being broken is also present.

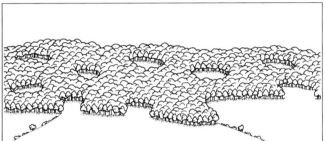

Phase one of a regularly spaced pattern.

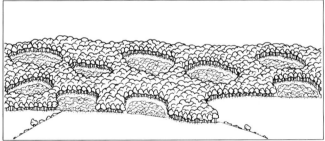

Phase two: the unity of the pattern is lost.

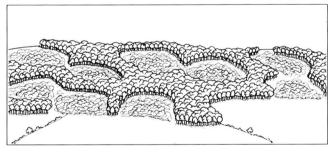

Phase three: the forest is completely fragmented.

b. Once again, a shaped coupe is retained and groups on the lower slopes designed in terms of size and position so that they eventually produce a coupe shape which follows landform.

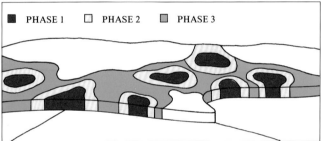

■ PHASE 1 □ PHASE 2 ▨ PHASE 3

The pattern of coupes and groups.

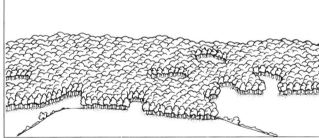

Phase one.

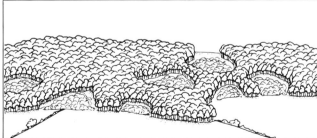

Phase two.

Phase three.

31

Skylines

Skylines are prominent and sensitive parts of any design, and are worth treating separately. The scale of skylines should generally be large, and they should be kept either predominantly open or wooded. The following points are common to all silvicultural systems.

Avoid — fringes, especially of scattered trees.

— breaking up convex skylines into small groups; have one or two coupes for preference and not more than three.

— fellings which divide convex landforms symmetrically.

Try to — position coupe boundaries near saddles.

— take coupe boundaries in a diagonal curve over skylines.

Where small coupes or group fellings are proposed, the skyline is best treated separately. Design coalescing belts to be felled in successive phases. Smaller regeneration groups can proceed lower down the slope where the scale of landscape is reduced.

Sections drawn from contour maps can be used to test whether the skyline will retain its continuous wooded appearance when seen from various viewpoints.

65. This wood has been partly felled leaving a scattered selection of trees on the skyline. They are insufficient to maintain the appearance of continous woodland.

66. A small woodland where heavy felling has resulted in a very fragmented canopy seen as a skyline in this gently rolling topography. The problem could have been eliminated if the sequence in Figure 67 had been observed.

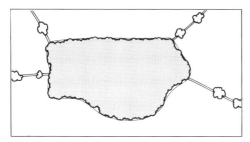

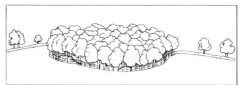

67a. A small broadleaved wood prior to regeneration.

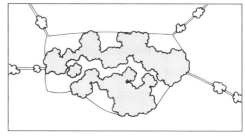

b. Early fellings maintain a continuous skyline.

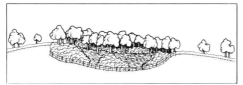

c. Later fellings retain the continuous skyline by careful choice of trees whose crowns coalesce as seen from the main viewpoint.

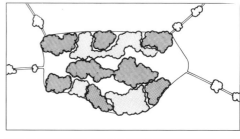

d. Eventually the regeneration creates a new skyline and the remaining trees can be removed.

68. These diagrams illustrate how topographic sections can be used to identify what areas need to be retained to maintain the appearance of a complete skyline from particular viewpoints. Two phases of felling are sufficient to ensure that an out of scale skyline is never exposed to view.

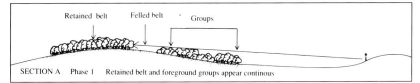

SECTION A   Phase 1   Retained belt and foreground groups appear continous

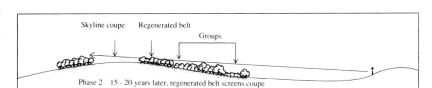

Phase 2   15 - 20 years later, regenerated belt screens coupe

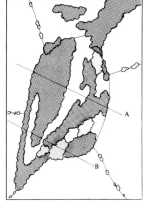

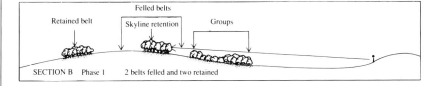

SECTION B   Phase 1   2 belts felled and two retained

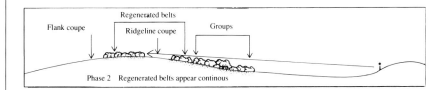

Phase 2   Regenerated belts appear continous

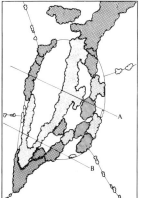

Belts

Edge belts of different species or retained trees are usually unsatisfactory. Groups of irregular size and spacing are better. Where edge belts already exist, take the first opportunity to break them into irregular sized groups or clumps of trees at varying spacings.

There are many examples of old shelterbelts that have become moribund, wind damaged and in need of regeneration. The worst cases are often very prominent, on skylines where they are most exposed. The best treatment is to select and fell stretches of shelterbelt and replant. Where the belt runs over a hill, break it in a saddle if possible. The shape and scale of belts can be improved at any time by planting adjacent ground to increase width and to introduce curved margins. Additional woodland planted nearby will increase the apparent scale, using nearness and coalescence.

69. An edge belt of broadleaves against a conifer forest. This is intrusive because it looks as though the conifers are being hidden whereas they have outgrown the broadleaves and can be seen over the top of them. The belt will be semi-transparent after felling and should be broken into irregular lengths.

70. *These sketches show how to reduce the impact of an intrusive screening belt.*

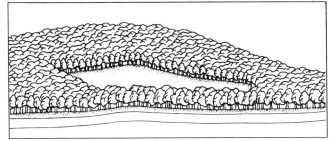

a. *An intrusive belt retained to screen a felling coupe from the road.*

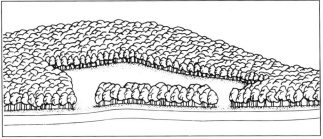

b. *Adjust the junction of the screen and coupe edges to give a more diagonal direction.*

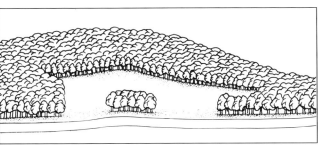

c. *A retention one-third of the size of the gaps should be located one-third of the way across. This leaves a rather large gap on the right.*

d. *A second retention one-third the width of and central one-third of the way across it leaves irregularly sized and spaced groups. N.B. Any additional retentions would repeat the formal effect of the belt.*

71a. *A straggly shelterbelt on a skyline.*

b. *Felling sections unrelated to landform look awkward, particularly on knolls.*

c. *Felling a complete section of the skyline is better - from saddle to saddle.*

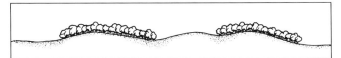

d. *Once the felled sections are regenerated the remainder can be felled and replanted.*

72. *A shelterbelt which has become moribund. Losses over the years have reduced the density of trees so that it looks tatty and in need of regeneration.*

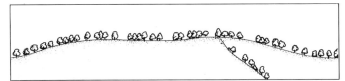

73a. *A straggly remnant belt along a ridge.*

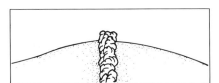

The end views.

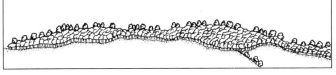

b. *Planting a new belt on both sides improves scale.*

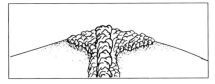

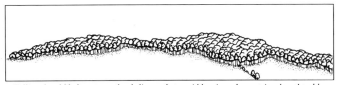

c. *Felling the old belt restores the skyline. . . but avoid leaving a bare strip when the old trees are felled by planting through them.*

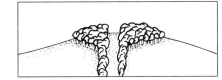

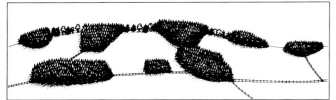

74a. A shelterbelt system where the ridge belts have become thin and scraggy requiring regeneration.

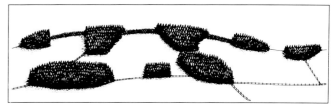

b. Felling and replanting the thinnest parts disrupts the flow of the skyline and creates symmetry among the clumps left unfelled.

c. A solution is to fell part of the entire skyline in two asymmetric sections leaving the remaining parts linked into the rest of the system. The felled sections are replanted.

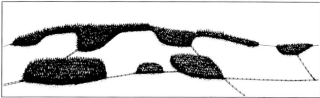

d. Once the replanted sections are able to provide shelter the rest of the system is felled and replanted with the exception of one clump. In this way the scale of the belt system is maintained and a degree of shelter is retained throughout the regeneration phase.

Retained Trees

Old trees retained on felled areas may benefit wildlife and landscape. This depends on their scale, distribution and individual attributes, and whether they increase diversity in terms of habitat or visually. The landscape considerations concerning retained trees seldom conflict with the requirements of wildlife. The latter should be sacrificed to landscape, or vice versa, only after examining a range of solutions that might satisfy both.

Trees of low sale value with well-formed crowns are candidates for retention if they form coherent groups or are located close to the edge of the coupe. An even scatter of single stems looks out of scale and 'spotty' and should be selectively felled to form distinct well-positioned groups. Groups in the central third of the coupe appear isolated and symmetrically placed. They should only be retained if they appear to be linked to the edge by other trees.

75. Trees retained on a felling coupe.

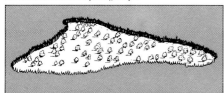

a. Individual trees scattered throughout the coupe have a spotty appearance.

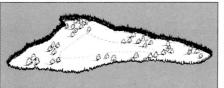

b. Discrete groups near the periphery of the coupe improve diversity and scale.

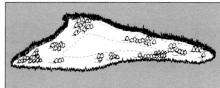

c. Dense groups improve scale and diversity further.

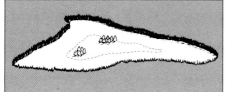

d. Groups in the central area of the coupe are likely to appear isolated and symmetrically placed...

e. ... unless linked to the edge by other groups.

DETAILED DESIGN ELEMENTS

Many lowland woods are seen predominantly from footpaths, bridleways or public roads. The internal landscape, seen in short range views, is often of great importance. The woodlands often contain a variety of open spaces, for recreation, wildlife conservation, archaeology, and a number of service requirements such as electricity and other wayleaves. Open space is necessary for woodland management, as deer glades, timber stacking sites and so on. These open spaces influence the internal landscape, as do operations such as fence erection and planting with treeshelters.

Edge Design

Though woodland edges and margins are physically the same, in design terms they are distinct. Margins define the shape of a space; the edge is a matter of individual elements of single trees and small groups. The edge detail is usually superimposed on a previously designed margin. Although external edges are the most obvious, the same detailed treatments should be applied within the woodland, wherever trees adjoin more or less open ground.

    The shape of the forest margin must be attractive, and completely designed before details of edge treatment are worked out. Edges, no matter how well designed, will not improve bad shapes.

    Where there is no existing pattern of trees in the surrounding landscape, the edge should reflect landform or the pattern of ground vegetation. There are useful pointers in the gradual changes from woodland to open ground in natural forests.

    In man-made woodlands edges can be made to look as natural as is practicable and varied in scale with the landscape.

    —By detailed shaping of the edge. The protrusions and indentations of the main mass of the woodland are important visual links and should follow landform in the same way as woodland shapes. They should be irregular in size and distribution to avoid unnatural symmetry.

    —By using species with different growth rates to vary tree height on the edge. This avoids a continuous wall effect, particularly with conifers. Create tapered edges by transitions from fast-growing conifers, through slower conifers and broadleaves, to shrub species. This should be done in appropriate places, along roadsides for example, or where edges cross prominent skylines or ridges.

    —By increasing tree spacing towards the outer edge of the wood. Wider spacing should be irregular, particularly in small-scale landscapes, or close to roads and paths. Regular spacing looks artificial. Treatment must be bold if it is not to be visually insignificant.

    —By establishing irregular outlying groups. These should be near enough to the woodland to be seen as part of it, not 'free-floating'. Position them to appear to be natural extensions. Avoid too many groups, which make the scale too small and appear too regular.

    —By planting individual trees close to the forest edge or to outlying groups, to link the woodland with open ground. Give them room to develop well-shaped crowns.

76. A good edge where irregularly spaced and sized groups and individual trees provide diversity and longer term structure.

77. Design of forest edge with layered profile.

a. Continuous strips of trees of different heights gives an edge a very artificial appearance.

b. Overlapping different layers in groups looks more interesting and unified; appropriate for medium to small-scale landscapes.

—By thinning to create a softer edge to felling areas, allowing the opening to penetrate into the adjoining stands. This can be further enhanced in sensitive areas by pruning dead branches to varying heights and so lessening the 'brown edge' effect, especially noticeable in conifers.

The opportunity should not be missed to establish ecologically and visually diverse edges at time of planting. It is cheaper to do it then and the results will be better, particularly where the edges cannot be thinned later because of the risk of windthrow.

The designer should have a clear understanding of the wildlife value of edges. An 'ecological edge' occurs at the boundary of two habitats or plant communities. Watercourses illustrate this, with a sequence of edges; aquatic vegetation gives way to bankside grasses and herbs, then to taller grass and small shrubs, then perhaps to larger shrubs and trees. Ecological edges also have a vertical component, with edges occurring between the different levels of shrub layers and tree crowns, for example.

The ecological value of an edge is almost always greater than the value of the interior of individual habitats adjoining. It lies in the range of plant life in a relatively small space, and in the ability of animals to use the neighbouring habitats, perhaps feeding in one and finding cover or nesting in another. Good landscape design can contribute to this through diversity of ground vegetation, shrub, understorey and canopy layers in various combinations. Variation in conditions of light and moisture provided by different ages, species and densities of trees in an irregular edge greatly increases the wildlife value of woodland. It also makes it look much more interesting.

78. Reducing the impact of a dark conifer edge.

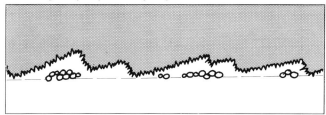

a. Varying a long edge of pine by a series of irregular steps in echelon with broadleaved groups kept sufficiently clear of deep shadows.

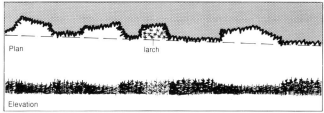

b. A long edge of pine varied with bold indentations to give shadow breaks (one filled with larch for colour contrast).

c. Reducing the visual impact of the solid 'wall' of dark conifers by 'off site' planting. This practice is only effective if viewpoints are limited.

79. How to unify the forest edge with outlying groups.

a. Undesirable slot between outlying groups and the forest.

b. Unsightly gap avoided by wrapping group around an extension to the forest.

c. Use overlapping groups . . .

d. . . . and slight indentations of the forest edge opposite the nearest groups.

The smaller scale of lowland hedgerow landscape means that detail is important. The irregular distribution of trees along the hedgerows should be echoed and emphasised in the woodland edge. Existing hedgerow trees in the woodland edge are of great value to landscape and wildlife. They should not be prematurely felled. Their crowns need space to develop, and adjacent planting should be kept far enough away so that young trees do not compete for light or overshadow and hide the crowns.

The size of large individual hedgerow trees is such that the loss of even a few has a major impact on the local landscape. The effects of Dutch elm disease illustrated this. The woodland edge should therefore be planned so that younger groups of trees, growing in open conditions, can in due course supply the successors to the present mature specimens. The even age and height of a plantation make it difficult to match the irregularity of a mature hedgerow. The diversity of the woodland edge should therefore be exaggerated. The amount of irregularity in the hedgerow pattern in the vicinity of the wood, the general density of trees in the hedgerows and the variation in their spacing suggest how woodland edge groups might be distributed.

It is easy to lose the continuity of the hedgerow pattern when adjoining woodland is felled, unless some individual trees and groups are retained. Whippy, one-sided trees are unsightly. It is best to identify trees to be retained well in advance of felling and give them space to develop their crowns fully.

Some ancient hedgerows are of great historic and botanical interest, sometimes associated with ancient boundaries and often characterised by a wide range of tree and shrub species. It is important to recognise these survivors and to conserve their special features. Adequate space should be left on either side for light to reach ground level and to allow them to be appreciated as contributors to the spirit of the place.

80. The edge of the woodland and its relation to hedgerows and hedgerow trees.

a. Where the density of hedgerow trees beside the wood is typical of the surrounding landscape some outlying trees should be planted in between hedgerow trees, of which a few should be replaced by groups to perpetuate the pattern.

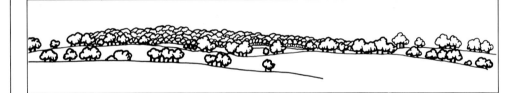

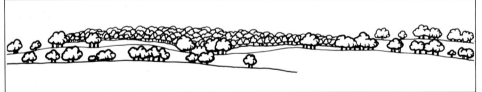

b. When there are fewer trees beside the wood, indentations in the edge and outlying groups should be used to enhance diversity.

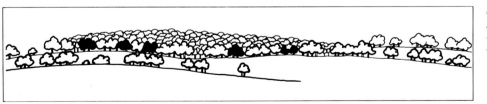

c. Where tree density is higher, selected groups of hedgerow trees should be felled and replaced in a pattern more typical of the surrounding hedgerows.

Design for Recreation

The management of woodlands close to or forming part of recreation facilities has to have clear aesthetic objectives if they are to be attractive. This applies particularly to the internal landscape of the woodlands and the planning of open spaces and views.

An important aspect of the internal landscape is the structure of the woodland itself; the variety of species, ages and arrangement of stands. This should be rich and varied, avoiding monotonous stretches of the same age, and allowing small areas of old trees to be retained to give a sense of age and continuity. Recreation and wildlife conservation values can be maintained or improved by developing the stand structure, in terms of overstorey, understorey, shrub and herb layers. A good shrub layer can increase the carrying capacity for recreational purposes and help in the management of visitors.

Open spaces for recreation should have a degree of privacy, to allow different groups to picnic, and still give a sense of continuity. The following measures are useful:

—— Ensure that the woodland edge is well shaped in relation to landform, and trees thinned, brashed and pruned if appropriate.

—— Identify one-third of the open area to be planted with broadleaves. The layout should exaggerate the openness and constriction of the space. Embellish the woodland and footpath edges with occasional groups, irregularly sized and spaced, with some as screen or barrier planting.

—— Having identified the broadleaved area, allocate two-thirds of it to one major species to grow to large size. Establish these quickly.

—— Allocate the remaining one-third to different combinations of small trees and shrubs in varied spacings and layers; have wider spacings and smaller species mainly, but not exclusively, nearer open space.

—— It is often undesirable to fell trees to create permanent open space in old broadleaved woodland. Views into the woods and the illusion of open space beneath the canopy can be developed by judicious tree pruning and some cutting in the understorey and shrub layers.

81. The setting in which woodland recreation in its many forms takes place is important. Here a pleasant glade with a varied edge and shape provides an ideal spot for a picnic.

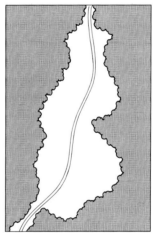

82a. Design for recreational purposes within a basic open space.

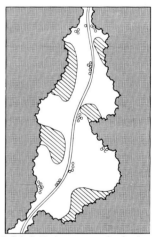

b. Sub-divide the open space by planting up to one-third. This creates smaller areas where different groups of people can enjoy themselves without interfering with each other.

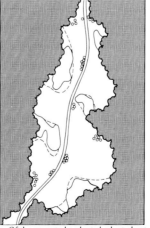

c. Of the areas to be planted, plant about two-thirds with one species, to keep the unity of the design and simplicity of management.

d. Of the remaining third, plant with a variety of trees and shrubs for good edge development and visual effect.

Views are an important aspect of open space and viewpoints should be identified and embodied in the woodland design. Trees in the foreground and middle ground should provide a setting for the view, rather than compete with it. Views within the woodland and out of it into the surrounding countryside help to orient the visitor. They take several forms, which include:

— Panoramic views, usually seen from high ground over steep slopes, should have little restriction in the fore or middle ground. Any trees in the foreground should have a gently curving edge to underline the view; this is more effective than an abrupt enframement.

— Feature views are dominated by one or a few eye-catching elements. The woodland should draw the eye to them.

— Focal views occur in valleys, with ridge lines directing the eye to the lower slopes. Overhanging trees can be helpful in emphasising the point of convergence.

— Canopy views utilise the trees as the overhead plane, and are best appreciated on foot.

— Filtered views are seen through an open screen of foreground trees. They must be used with caution, as the screen often closes up quickly and obscures the view. An open view is often preferable, particularly if a series of openings can be made alongside roads or paths.

83. Types of view.

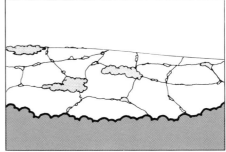

a. Panoramic view.

b. Feature view.

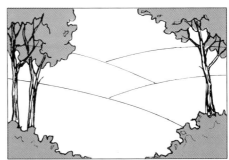

c. Focal view.

d. Canopied view.

e. Filtered view.

Roadside Design

Woodlands beside public roads should give an interesting sequence of views with a succession of varied spaces. Motorists are unaware of a wealth of fine detail. Design of public road edges must be on a broad scale, related to the average speed of the traffic.

— Keep landscape simple and undistracting at junctions, sharp bends, steep hills and blind summits. The driver's attention must be on the road.

— The woodland edge can be brought closer to the road on bends and steep hills, where the constricted space enhances the sense of movement. Edges should be further back on gentle alignments, with occasional features near the road.

— Where existing edges are straight, parallel to the road, equidistant on either side and strongly enclosing, improve them when an opportunity arises and create more interesting and varied edges.

— The sides of views opening through the woodland from public roads should splay out at acute angles. Narrow parallel-sided openings at right angles to the road will be missed by car occupants. The same principle applies to rides and footpaths, to a lesser degree.

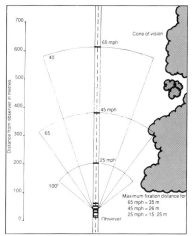

84. Angles of vision as seen from moving vehicles of various speeds.

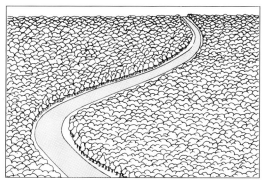

85a. A curving road passing through a woodland with a boring parallel edge.

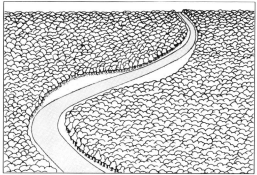

b. A degree of variation is introduced on the outside of bends but the space is still uninteresting.

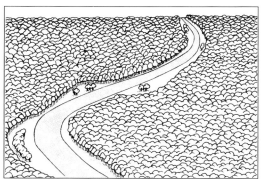

c. Rather more spatial variation together with some punctuating detail is introduced.

d. Much more generous openings off the edge and bolder groups give a strong sense of rhythm.

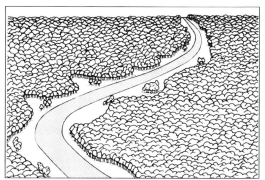

e. The edge has become rather too fragmented and scale too small.

f. Too much variation at too small a scale creates a boring diffuse edge similar to a.

86. A well laid out roadside where recent work has been carried out, showing the shape and scale of the spaces, retained features, and glimpses into the canopy.

Ride Design

Rides are often a traditional feature of lowland woodlands, valuable for sporting and general access. Their wildlife importance can be considerable, and in some parts of the countryside they may be the only extensive areas of unimproved grassland to survive. The relative priorities of informal recreation and sport, wildlife and landscape will vary, depending on the locality.

The forest edge dominates the appearance of rides. Rides should vary in width, shape and direction, designed in response to landform in a similar fashion to other internal open spaces. They should be gently curved with a succession of spaces of different sizes.

Setting back the forest edge to allow more sunlight to reach the ground increases the visual interest of rides, and the range of wildlife habitats. It is important to take into account the height of the tree crop on the south side of the ride edge. The distance from the forest edge to the ride must equal the height of the trees to enable sunlight to fall on the ride for an appreciable length of time (Carter and Anderson, 1987; Ferris-Kaan, 1991). Layout of the final edge shape is the first step.

Amounts of light reaching the ground can be increased by cutting 'bays' in the ride edges. These should be irregularly spaced, varied in size, and with their backs not parallel to the ride.

They should be positioned so that they partially overlap, not opposite each other. East-west orientation is preferred for maximum sunshine on level ground.

Having defined the edge shape, design a path of mown grass, passing irregularly from one side of the ride to the other. Groups of broadleaved trees, tall and small shrubs and varied areas of rough grass should be located and combined in an irregular, interlocking pattern. Parallel strips of trees, shrubs and grass are dull.

Ride junctions, particularly those at right angles, should be adjusted as areas are felled and restocked. Junctions can be substantially improved by forming asymmetric glades.

Many of the above points apply equally to design along woodland roads and paths, though it may be more difficult to realign the space defined by the woodland edge or to block long views. Where long stretches of road are heavily used by visitors, the scale of the roadside space may be reduced by planting occasional groups of large broadleaves close to the road, at points where the road will not suffer from surface wetness.

87. Long straight rides can be dull places for both wildlife and visitors. When designing a ride layout this sequence should be followed:

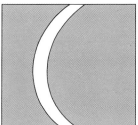
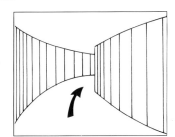

a. vary direction and. . .

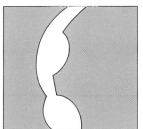
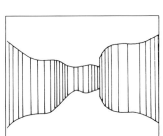

b. vary width but. . .

c. avoid symmetry and. . .

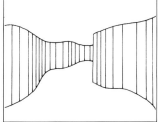

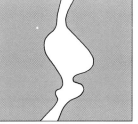
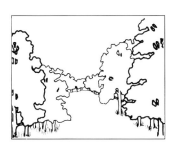

d. vary the scale of spaces and then. . .

e. increase the diversity in the edge.

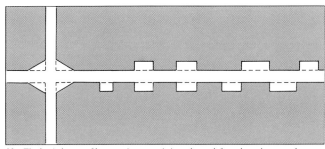

88a. The basic layout of bays cut into an existing edge or left unplanted can produce artificial effects.

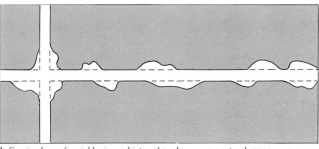

b. Curving bays of variable size and interval produce a more natural appearance.

89. Improving or creating a ride design which is good for wildlife and for walkers.

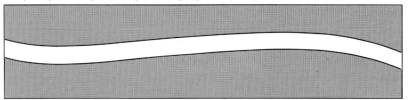

a. An existing parallel-edged ride, or basic alignment.

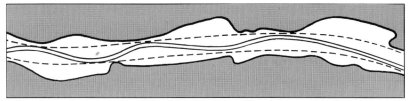

b. Shape the woodland edge to vary width and direction of spaces. Vary alignment of the path within the original ride.

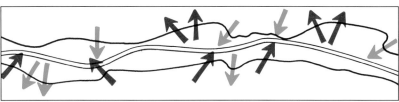

c. Decide where spaces need to be constricted or expanded to provide sequences, shelter or more sunlight. Use landform where possible.

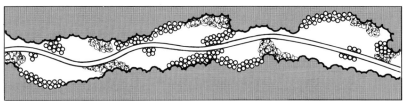

d. Emphasise constrictions of space to varying degrees by planting broadleaved trees and shrubs and emphasise expansion of space by heavy thinning and pruning of edges, or by lower density planting, where glades are wider. Add occasional groups where the path crosses an extensive space, e.g. for more than forty metres.

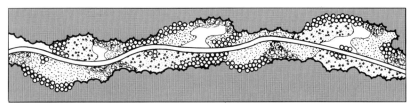

e. If greater conservation value or visual diversity is required residual areas may be managed as low shrubs or coppice with the remainder left as rough grass. Smaller alcoves, especially on the sunny side of the ride may be left and mown to provide areas for recreation.

90. The design of ride junctions.

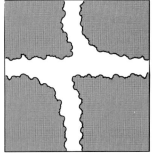 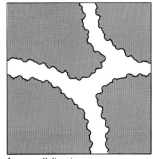 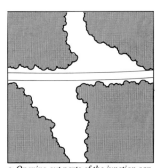 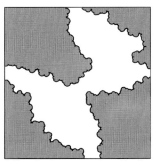

a. By aligning cross-junctions views can be terminated in two directions...

b. ... or all directions.

c. Opening out parts of the junction can terminate views (here shown at a road/ ride junction) and provide glades for conservation.

d. Here the views are terminated in all directions with glades for recreation or conservation built in also.

Design of Streamsides

Streamsides should have thriving natural bankside vegetation to minimise erosion and protect water quality. Unplanted streamside open spaces should be irregular, with the edges designed to link across the space at key points. The aim should be to have an irregular distribution of waterside broadleaved trees, so that about 50% of the stream is in full sunlight, the rest receiving dappled shade. In predominantly conifer woodlands continuous strips of streamside broadleaves are as inappropriate as corridors of open ground.

Open spaces near streamsides can serve a useful function as deer glades. They are best designed as a succession of glades at least 100 m long, screened from each other by tree groups overlapping the streamside space.

Where streams emerge from the lower margin of woodland in steep country, the streamside space should be widened in an asymmetrical bell-mouth shape. This is particularly important where streams meet lake shores.

91. A stream with well developed bankside vegetation being managed to maximise water quality, aquatic life and the wildlife value of the corridor.

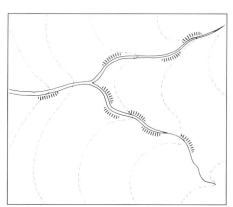

92a. A stream in an area ready to be planted.

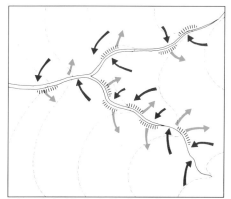

b. An analysis of the detailed landform adjacent to the stream.

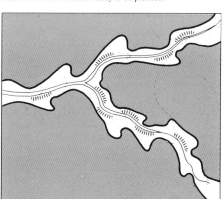

c. The basic woodland canopy edge designed to follow the landform.

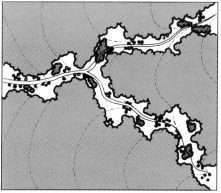

d. The detail of clumps, groups and individual trees is filled in to create the dapple shade requirements.

Design around Lakes

Woodlands around lakes and reservoirs are particularly sensitive because of the quality of the flat reflective water surface. Continuous woodland around a lake tends to form a dark band between the lighter sky and water. Open ground, with its intermediate colour and texture, can unite the landscape. An interlocking pattern of woodland and open ground achieves the best effect.

The appearance of the natural line of the water's edge is apt to be lost when trees are planted too close to the shore. This is most obvious where a promontory extends into the lake. Keep promontories as open space, allowing views across to water beyond. The woodland should be brought to the water's edge at some points, otherwise it will seem to float on a ribbon of open space. Groups of trees that overlap with the forest edge and overhang the water help to make the necessary links between water and woodland.

Streams and lakesides are important for wildlife, and the requirements of the latter have to be balanced with those of landscape. The ideal is to establish a broad pattern of woodland edges, with the dense tree cover merging into lower, more open, trees and shrubs, then open space — which may be wetland or waterside vegetation — so giving a gradual change of vertical scale.

93. A woodland lake showing an interesting, well structured edge and a variety of spaces and edge species.

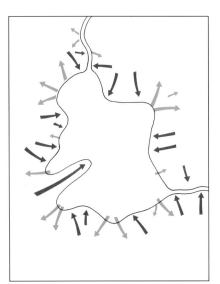

94a. A lake falling within a new woodland area, analysed in terms of landform around its margin.

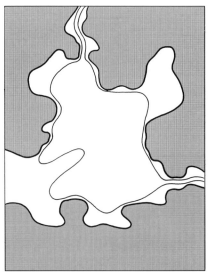

b. The basic woodland canopy edge is designed. A balance between woodland mass, open space and the water plane should be sought.

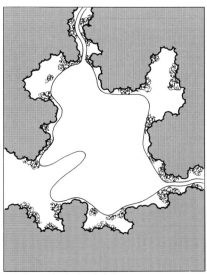

c. Following b, the detail of edge treatment, groups and clumps of smaller trees and shrubs may be inserted.

Power Lines

Power lines are similar to rides in their visual effect. There are many instances where power lines have been deliberately routed through woodland with the misguided notion that this would hide them. The open wayleave corridor is often a greater visual affront than the towers carrying the line. Power lines should be planned to follow open space, and to run alongside, not through, woodland. It is up to woodland managers and planning authorities to insist on this. In much frequented or sensitive localities it is reasonable to demand that power lines be kept out of the area altogether.

Where there really is no alternative route, a power line through woodland should:

— avoid areas of landscape sensitivity or be put underground;

— not follow the line of sight of important views;

— be kept in valleys or depressions;

— not divide a hill into two similar parts where it crosses over a summit;

— cross skylines or ridges where they dip to a low point;

— follow alignments diagonal to the contour as far as possible;

— be inflected upwards in hollows and downwards on ridges.

95. A parallel-sided, narrow powerline corridor cutting through a woodland area. Forest of Dean, Gloucs.

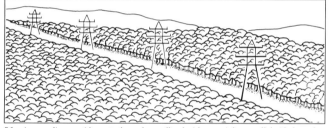

96a. A powerline corridor cuts through woodland with a straight, parallel-sided swathe.

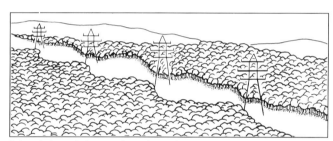

b. Introducing variation according to basic rules produces a symmetrical effect.

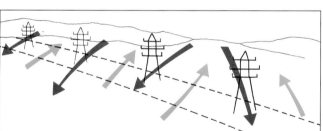

c. Analyse the landform using visual forces.

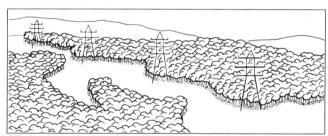

d. Design the corridor to interlock with the forest and follow landforms thus avoiding a parallel or symmetrical effect.

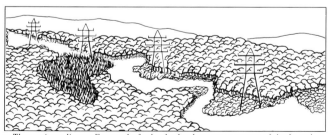

e. The persistent linear effect can be further broken by areas or groups of shrubs and coppice either increasing interlock further or breaking the line completely.

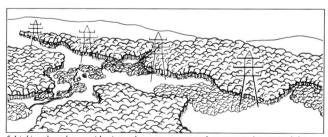

f. Linking the pylon corridor into other open spaces such as streams integrates it into the landscape further.

Within the woodland the power line should seem to pass through a series of irregular spaces. The woodland should appear to meet across the open space in some places so that the corridor does not split it completely. A uniform width of corridor is not obligatory; trees can be planted closer to the line opposite pylons than in mid-span, where the line hangs lower and swings more. Smaller trees and shrubs can be grown closer still, as an extension of the woodland edge towards the power line.

Coppice is useful to disguise the base of pylons and to form overlapping tongues of small trees to contain any views. This edge should be designed to form irregular spaces with irregular tree heights, avoiding severe vertical edges, particularly of conifers.

The aim should be a corridor of varying character and width, swinging from one side of the line to the other. Avoid irregular but parallel edges, or irregular but symmetrical spaces. Exit points should be gently asymmetrical bell-mouths. Felling areas should link with and across the power line corridor and give the impression of greater irregularity.

Similar considerations apply to the design of pipelines or any other service corridors through the forest that have to be kept clear of trees.

97a. A view inside a parallel-sided straight corridor is very boring and unnatural.

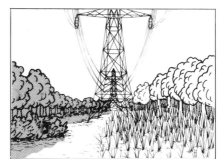

b. The re-designed corridor is asymmetric with a well developed edge structure. The sinous space deflects the eye from the powerline.

Smaller Open Spaces

Small open spaces within the woodland are valuable sources of diversity for both recreation and wildlife. These spaces should have edges that define the space without being claustrophobic. Proportions are important; dense edges of conifers can be oppressive if the width of the space is less than three times tree height, especially in narrow valleys. A width of ten times tree height loses the sense of enclosure altogether. Enclosed space within these limits makes a comfortable change and contrasts with more open ground.

Edges of internal spaces should draw the eye easily from one part of the space to another, while emphasising any focal points. They should vary the width of the space, avoiding geometric or symmetric shapes. Trees and shrubs judiciously placed within the space provide points of interest and can soften abrupt junctions of vertical wooded edge with the plane of the ground, as well as adding useful elements of diversity.

Open space around rocks and crags will depend on their size and importance as landscape features and the steepness of the ground below. Leave sufficient space so that when trees are fully grown they do not obscure features. The space should be designed in the same manner as other forest shapes.

98. A small open space adds interest to the woodland.

Deer Glades

Many woodlands have a deer population and control of numbers may be necessary. Deer glades are required for this purpose, sited where deer can be shot in safety. The best glades are those that deer already frequent, with shelter and browse species available (Ratcliffe, 1985).

Deer glades also serve a useful function as open spaces of general benefit to wildlife. Edges should look natural, shaped to follow landform where present, and with varied areas of herb and shrub vegetation around the edge and extending into the glade.

99. A ride being used as a deer glade. With further work of widening the space and improving the diversity of vegetation it could be a useful addition to the open space content of the woodland.

Landscape and Forest Operations

Fences

A fence line is often visible as a boundary between contrasting vegetation, caused by different degrees of grazing pressure. This looks artificial if the fence encloses geometric shapes, particularly where it encloses areas that lie outside the woodland edge. Appearance can sometimes be improved by running the fence on an irregular diagonal alignment, so that the trees hide the fence as they grow up. This approach is worth bearing in mind when negotiating for the purchase or sale of land. It may be difficult to put into practice on existing ownership boundaries. An alternative in prominent situations is to erect fences on well designed alignments inside the legal boundaries, defining the latter as necessary by unobtrusive but permanent markers.

The effects of unsightly fences can be reduced by:

— positioning fences where there is least visual impact; for example in hollows, away from skylines, or close to the woodland edge;

— running fences diagonally to the contours, not following them or going straight uphill;

— making fences follow landform;

— changing direction at irregular intervals, in scale with the landscape, and avoiding right angles;

— following the forest edge closely, or else leaving an intervening area of open ground of suitable shape and appropriate scale;

— using high-tensile spring steel fencing, particularly along roadsides. This uses fewer posts and looks better than post and wire fences;

— once the trees are well established, re-siting stock fences to alignments running inside the wood, among the trees. Fences on public road sides can be similarly re-positioned. If they can be dispensed with altogether, so much the better.

Lowland woodland fences often have to follow straight field boundaries, the harsh lines of which can be softened by shaping the planted area within the straight fences. The resulting areas of rough semi-natural vegetation on the unplanted ground form most useful gradations from the field headlands to the edge of the trees.

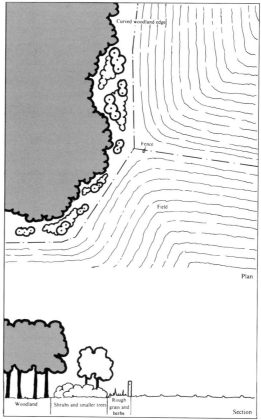

100. Designing a woodland edge within a regular fence line against agricultural fields.

Treeshelters

Planting in rigid translucent plastic tubes enables individual trees to be established quickly. Even when used with sensitivity they look very artificial, especially in large numbers. Temporary fencing to exclude browsing animals, with correct use of herbicides to secure rapid early tree growth, is cheaper on larger areas and looks better.

Use shelters to establish small groups and individual trees. They should:

— be of an unobtrusive colour, to blend with surround-ings. Russet browns or olive greens are best. Avoid white or garnish greens.

— be positioned in irregular fashion, not in geometric patterns. Straight rows are unnecessary because the position of the trees is clear;

— be well staked and securely erected. Leaning shelters give an impression of dereliction and incompetence.

Once the trees are well established and the shelters are no longer required, remove stakes and decayed plastic from the site.

101a. White treeshelters stand out intrusively against any background.

b. Olive green and brown shelters, here set out in drifts, blend better with the natural vegetation colours substantially reducing their visual impact.

Design for Game

The overriding objectives in woodlands managed for game are to provide an environment for safe shooting and to provide suitable conditions in the wood for the reproduction, growth and protection of the animals concerned. These requirements can be met by woods where the design follows the principles described above for small woodlands. The effect on the landscape is the same, whatever the reason for planting.

The shape of the layout becomes increasingly important on steeper ground and with larger areas of woodland. The shape should reflect the form of the ground so that edges and boundaries rise uphill in hollows and fall on convex slopes. Boundaries should not run straight up the slope or follow contours horizontally. Right angles should be avoided, except on flatter ground where traditional rectangular enclosure boundaries dominate.

Asymmetric curved diagonal shapes, with varied widths of belts, represent the ideal. Cost-conscious managers may be tempted to favour straight-fenced compact shapes, but with a little imagina-tion the formality of the square and rectangle can be avoided. Trapezoids, uneven triangles and other shapes with sides of varying length offer a possible compromise, combining informality and economy.

There are many designs for the internal layout of woods for game management, such as described in *Woodlands for Pheasants* (McCall, 1988). The game covert edge usually contains large conifers for shelter; medium sized broadleaved trees and shrubs for food; and a hedge of some sort to keep out the wind. Planting these constituents in continuous belts gives a very formal series of parallel layers. Except for the hedge, they should be laid out as irregular overlapping groups.

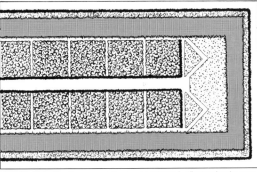

102. Rectangular shapes are intrusive in all but the flattest landscapes.

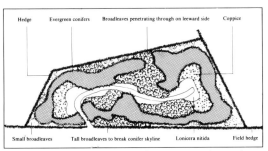

103. An irregular geometric layout such as an asymmetric trapezium minimises fencing complications while providing a shape within which to plant a covert with more irregular, interlocking shapes.

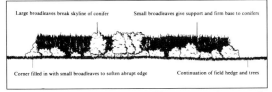

104. The edge of the covert designed at 103. An asymmetric pattern of overlapping groups results in a more natural appearance.

REFERENCES

Carter, C. I. and Anderson, M. A. , 1987 — Enhancement of Lowland Forest Ridesides and Roadsides to Benefit Wild Plants and Butterflies.
Forestry Commission Research Information Note 126.

Evans, J. , 1984 — Silviculture of Broadleaved Woodland.
Forestry Commission Bulletin 62. HMSO, London.

Ferris-Kaan , R . (ed) , 1991 — Edge Management in Woodlands.
Forestry Commission Occasional Paper 28.
Forestry Commission, Edinburgh.

Forestry Commission , 1985 — Guidelines for the Management of Broadleaved Woodland.
Forestry Commission, Edinburgh.

Hibberd, B.G. (ed.), 1988 — Farm Woodland Practice.
Forestry Commission Handbook 3. HMSO, London.

Hibberd, B.G. (ed.), 1991 — Forestry Practice.
Forestry Commission Handbook 6. HMSO, London.

Hart, C. , 1991 — Practical Forestry for the Agent and Surveyor.
Third Edition. Alan Sutton, Stroud.

Lucas, O. W. R. , 1991 — The Design of Forest Landscapes.
Oxford University Press, Oxford.

McCall, I. , 1988 — Woodlands for Pheasants.
The Game Conservancy, Fordingbridge.

Rackham, O. , 1986 — The History of the Countryside.
J.M. Dent, London.

Rackham, O. , 1990 — Trees and Woods in the British Landscape.
J.M. Dent, London.

Ratcliffe, P. R. , 1985 — Glades for Deer Control in Upland Forests.
Forestry Commission Leaflet 86. HMSO, London.

Appendix 1
How to Assess Landscape Character

The assessment of landscape character highlights those features that should govern the subsequent design of woodland planting or felling, so that the woodland will blend well with the surrounding landscape. These features help to determine whether the landscape would be seriously compromised by the proposed woodland operations, and whether they are appropriate in that particular landscape.

When identifying the elements of landscape character it is most useful to make simple annotated sketches. If this is not possible for any reason, written descriptions become more important. These must be done thoroughly and carefully if mistakes are to be avoided. Photographs from principal viewpoints are essential, as aide-memoires and to support written descriptions. Rank the viewpoints in order of importance; this helps in deciding where assessments and design studies should be made.

An assessment in the following format will ensure that important points are covered.

1. Landform
This is likely to be a significant characteristic in all but the flattest enclosed landscapes.

Shape

Describe the shape, e.g. rounded, irregular, smooth rolling jagged, etc. Surface modelling may be important; a rounded landform may have small bumps or knolls in places.

Scale

This can be large, i.e. with broad, sweeping scale with wide views: small scale, with narrow, confined short views: or somewhere in between. Note that:

— Scale is usually smaller in valley bottoms and larger towards the open hill tops. It can vary substantially within a landscape.

— Keep the assessment of landform scale separate in your mind from the scale of land use and vegetation patterns.

2. Vegetation
Patterns of semi-natural or cultivated vegetation are important features because of the shapes and colours they display. Trees and existing woods can have a great impact by creating enclosures, or they can be incidental features.

Semi-natural vegetation

Note the types of shapes in the landscape — irregular, broken, flowing, patchwork, etc. Note also the scale of the patterns compared with the landform, for example there may be small intricate patterns on a large-scale hillside. Record the colours, especially seasonal colours such as those of bracken, heather and so on.

Cultivated vegetation

Is there a distinct pattern of fields? (Ancient, planned or with the pattern breaking down.) Are the crops or pasture in a particular location in the landscape, such as in the valley bottom? Do the fields extend up hillsides, and if so, in what way? Note the shapes, scales and colours of fields, enclosures and other cultivated areas.

Trees and woods

Do hedgerows form strong patterns, do they coalesce to give a well wooded appearance? Are hedgerow patterns intact, largely intact, breaking down or very weak. Do existing belts of trees form patterns along streams or roadsides? Are existing woods part of a well defined pattern (branching, enclosing, linear, clumpy)? Are the woods small irregular woodlands in an ancient field pattern or plantations in a planted landscape? Are the woods coniferous, broadleaved or mixed?

3. Natural features
Rocks, streams and other features are useful elements of diversity in the landscape, and can contribute a lot to landscape character.

Rocks

Are there rock outcrops, crags, cliffs, etc., in the area? Are these particularly distinctive, or common in the landscape? Are they isolated or grouped? Are they small scale compared with the landform?

Streams

Are there any major rivers or streams? How are they spaced? Are they straight or meandering, deeply incised or running through a flat valley floor? Do stream courses form a vertical parallel pattern on hillsides?

4. Man-made features
These can be important elements which should be built into a design; or they may compromise the landscape quality and character.

Roads

These can be unsightly linear features as well as important public access routes. Is the alignment sympathetic or parallel on hillsides?

Lakes, ponds and wet areas

Identify all open water, wet areas, marshland or areas seasonally under water.

Walls, dykes, fences and hedges

Enclosure boundaries can enhance and reinforce the field patterns, and have an important effect on overall landscape character. This may compete with the landform and vegetation pattern in some circumstances. Note the shape and scale of the field pattern. The condition of hedges, walls, etc., may be important and should be recorded (intact, breaking down non-existing).

Buildings

These can be useful features, as elements of diversity and as cultural markers. They may need to be given breathing space. Record their importance; an old house may have considerable architectural merit, or it may be one of many similar examples in the area, of no particular value. Note their location and how they relate to landform, field pattern, roads, trees and woods and other features.

Power lines and other services

The corridors required by these features can be highly intrusive, as can the pylons, pipes, etc., themselves. Note how the alignment relates to the landform. Does the corridor follow a hollow? Does it cut across the skyline in a particularly awkward place?

Other features should be similarly recorded. These can include radio and television masts, railway lines, old mine and quarry workings, spoil heaps, and so on.

5. Cultural and historical associations

These can vary widely, from views of downland chalk carvings to a scene which Constable is reputed to have painted. These should be recorded. It may take some historical research to verify and place them in perspective.

Appendix 2
LANDSCAPE CHARACTER ASSESSMENT FORM

Describe and evaluate the dominant or important elements of
landscape character of the site and surrounding landscape. Make
sketches from significant viewpoints, and take photographs to act as
a record and as an aide-memoire.

Which is more important: landform or land use pattern?

Make notes on the following:

Landform

Shape

Scale

Vegetation

Semi-natural vegetation

Cultivated vegetation

Trees and woods

Natural Features

Rocks

Streams

Lakes, ponds, wet areas

Man-made Features

Roads

Walls, dykes, hedges, fences

Buildings

Power lines and other services

Other features

Any Known Cultural or Historical Associations

Now write a brief pen - picture of the landscape based on the above notes.

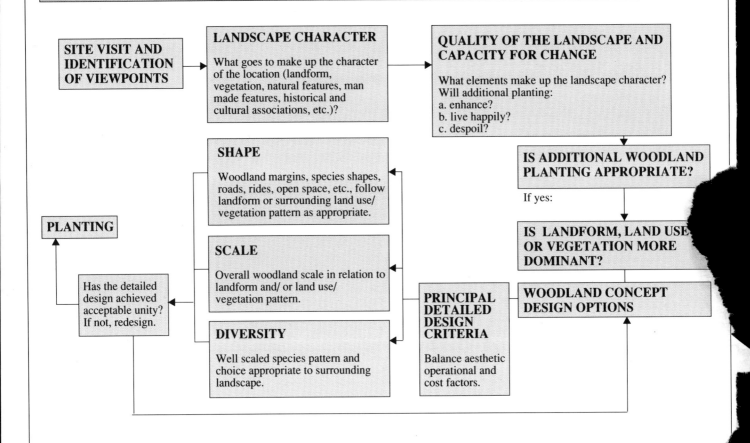

ASSESSMENT AND DESIGN PROCESS
NEW WOODLAND PLANTING

SITE VISIT AND IDENTIFICATION OF VIEWPOINTS

LANDSCAPE CHARACTER

What goes to make up the character of the location (landform, vegetation, natural features, man made features, historical and cultural associations, etc.)?

QUALITY OF THE LANDSCAPE AND CAPACITY FOR CHANGE

What elements make up the landscape character?
Will additional planting:
a. enhance?
b. live happily?
c. despoil?

IS ADDITIONAL WOODLAND PLANTING APPROPRIATE?

If yes:

IS LANDFORM, LAND USE OR VEGETATION MORE DOMINANT?

WOODLAND CONCEPT DESIGN OPTIONS

SHAPE

Woodland margins, species shapes, roads, rides, open space, etc., follow landform or surrounding land use/vegetation pattern as appropriate.

SCALE

Overall woodland scale in relation to landform and/ or land use/vegetation pattern.

DIVERSITY

Well scaled species pattern and choice appropriate to surrounding landscape.

PRINCIPAL DETAILED DESIGN CRITERIA

Balance aesthetic operational and cost factors.

PLANTING

Has the detailed design achieved acceptable unity? If not, redesign.

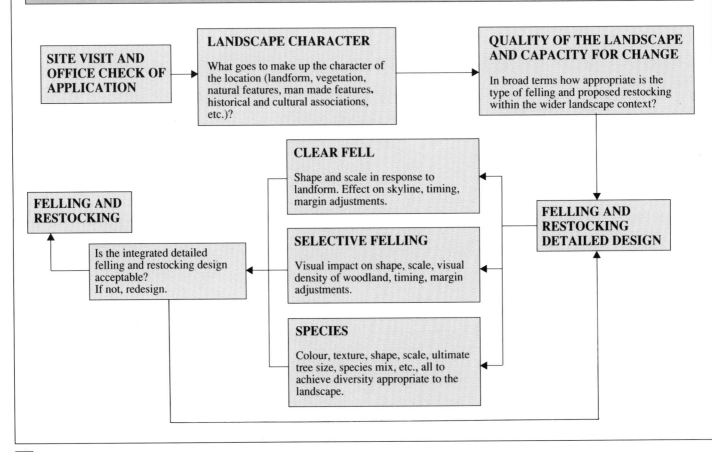

ASSESSMENT AND DESIGN PROCESS
LOWLAND FELLING AND RESTOCKING

SITE VISIT AND OFFICE CHECK OF APPLICATION

LANDSCAPE CHARACTER

What goes to make up the character of the location (landform, vegetation, natural features, man made features, historical and cultural associations, etc.)?

QUALITY OF THE LANDSCAPE AND CAPACITY FOR CHANGE

In broad terms how appropriate is the type of felling and proposed restocking within the wider landscape context?

FELLING AND RESTOCKING DETAILED DESIGN

CLEAR FELL

Shape and scale in response to landform. Effect on skyline, timing, margin adjustments.

SELECTIVE FELLING

Visual impact on shape, scale, visual density of woodland, timing, margin adjustments.

SPECIES

Colour, texture, shape, scale, ultimate tree size, species mix, etc., all to achieve diversity appropriate to the landscape.

FELLING AND RESTOCKING

Is the integrated detailed felling and restocking design acceptable?
If not, redesign.